LEVEL E

CONTENTS

UNIT 1 — Consonant Variants, Letter Combinations, Syllables

Poem "Fiddle-Faddle" by Eve Merriam 3

Home Letter 4

Sounds of **k, qu, kn** 5-6
Sounds of **ch** 7
Sounds of **c, g** 8-10
Words with the **f** Sound 11
Sounds of **s** 12
Sounds of **wh** 13
Words with the **sh** Sound 14
Sounds of **th** 15
Sounds of **wh, sh, th** 16

Review Consonant Variants, Letter Combinations, Syllables
Reading: "Birds With a Sense of Humor" . . . 17
Writing: Travel Brochure 18

Sounds of **sc, gn** 19-20
Sounds of **r (rh, wr, ear, air)** 21-24
Words with **ild, ind, ost, old** 25-26
Syllables 27-28
Review Letter Combinations and Sounds
Reading: "Tornadoes!" 29
Writing: An Interview 30

Unit Checkup 31-32

UNIT 2 — Vowel Pairs, Digraphs, Diphthongs, Syllables

Activity **Find the Hidden Treasure** 33

Home Letter 34

Vowel Pairs **ai, ay, ee, ei, oa, oe, ow** 35-40
Vowel Digraphs **ea, ei, ey, au, aw, ie,
    oo, ui** 41-50
Review Vowel Pairs and Digraphs
Reading: "Flying Symbols" 51

Writing: A Description 52

Diphthongs **oi, oy, ou, ow, ew**; Syllables . . . 53-58
Review Diphthongs
Reading: "Watching the Skies" 59
Writing: A Travel Report 60

Unit Checkup 61-62

UNIT 3 — Prefixes

Activity **Secret Message** 63

Home Letter 64

Units of Meaning in Words 65-66
Prefixes **un, dis, ir, in, im,
    en, mis, mal, pre, pro** 67-74
Review Prefixes
Reading: "Nothing Is Impossible" 75
Writing: Advice Column 76

Prefixes **re, ex, fore, post, over** 77-82
Prefixes **co, com, con, sub,
    mid, bi, tri** 83-88
Review Prefixes
Reading: "He's a Tiger!" 89
Writing: A Poster 90

Unit Checkup 91-92

UNIT 4

Roots, Compounds, Possessives, Contractions, Syllables

Poem "At the Science Fair" 93

Home Letter 94

Roots pos, pel, pul, port, ject, aud, dict, duct, duce, duc, scribe, script, spec, spect, mit, miss, fac, fect, fic, feit .. 95-100
Compound Words 101-102
Possessives 103-104
Contractions 105-106
Syllables 107-108

Review Roots, Compounds, Possessives, Contractions
Reading: "Diary Entry" 109
Writing: A Letter 110

Unit Checkup 111-112

UNIT 5

Suffixes

Activity Find the Modern Conveniences 113

Home Letter 114

Suffixes er, or, ist, ward, en, ize, er, est, ee, eer, ent, ant, ful, ness ... 115-122
Suffixes hood, ship, ment, able, ible, ion, ation, ition, ance, ence, ive, ity 123-130

Review Suffixes
Reading: "Helping Out" 131
Writing: A Project Plan 132

Unit Checkup 133-134

UNIT 6

Suffixes and Plurals

Poem "Fun With More Than One!" ... 135

Home Letter 136

Suffixes that Alter Base-Word Spellings .. 137-146
Plurals 147-152
Syllabication 153-156

Review Suffixes, Plurals
Reading: "Wilma Mankiller" 157
Writing: A Speech 158

Unit Checkup 159-160

UNIT 7

Dictionary Skills, Multi-meaning Words

Activity Comic Strip 161

Home Letter 162

Alphabetizing 163-164
Using the Dictionary 165-168
Multi-meaning Words (Homographs) 169-170

Review Dictionary Skills, Multi-meaning Words
Reading: "What's Real?" 171
Writing: An Article 172

Unit Checkup 173-174

Definitions and Rules 175-176

Fiddle Faddle

Riddle me no,
riddle me yes,
what is the secret
of sweet success?

Said the razor, "Be keen."
"String along," said the bean.
"Push" said the door.
"Be polished" said the floor.
Said the piano, "Stand upright and grand."
"Be on the watch," said the second hand.

"Be cool," said the ice cube.
"Be bright," said the TV tube.
"Bounce back," said the yo-yo.
"Be well bred," said the dough.
"Plug," said the stopper.
"Shine," said copper.

"Be game," said the quail.
"Make your point," said the nail.
"Have patience," said the M.D.
"Look spruce," said the tree.
"Press on," said the stamp.
"Shed some light," said the lamp.
"Oh, just have a good head,"
the cabbage said.

—*Eve Merriam*

What's your favorite piece of advice in this poem?

Critical Thinking

Home Letter

Dear Family,

In the next few weeks, your child will be learning the different sounds associated with vowels and consonants. Following are some activities that you might enjoy sharing.

At-Home Activities

▶ Read the poem "Fiddle Faddle" on the other side of this letter with your child to feel the rhyme and rhythm of the language used in the poem.

▶ Ask your child to find the words with the sounds of s, k, qu, sh, wh, th, g, and r in the poem. Then ask your child to complete another verse of the poem. Post the child's additional verse in a prominent place.

▶ With your child, discuss what success means in your family. Then, brainstorm ways that success can be achieved. Have your child create a poster to illustrate these paths to success. Hang the poster as a reminder to everyone in your family.

Book Corner

Another way to extend the learning experience is to read aloud with your child. Here are two poetry collections that you can probably find in the library.

Poetry from A to Z
by Paul B. Janeczko

Poets comment candidly on their work in this useful and encouraging resource for beginining poets.

Remembering and Other Poems
by Myra C. Livingston

Enjoy these forty-five imaginative poems that explore how ordinary sights can provoke playful journeys through the imagination.

Sincerely,

Name _____

> Circle the letter or letters that stand for the **k** sound in each word in the box. Then use the words to complete the sentences.

back	black	blacksmith	jackets		
kept	kettles	kinds	knack	look	
pockets	quick	techniques	thick	unique	

1. The early English settlers in America wore simple clothing that was often tan,

   gray, or _____ .

2. Native Americans showed them which _____ of plants could be used for dying cloth.

3. Bark, roots, seeds, and berries were sometimes boiled in large _____ to create shades of yellow, red, and brown.

4. The plain clothing of these settlers often had no decoration on the front or _____ .

5. Children were dressed to _____ like small adults.

6. Women sewed clothes from cloth made with different _____ , such as spinning and weaving.

7. Clothing was also made from animal skins and fur, which _____ people warm in winter.

8. Because materials were scarce, the settlers had a _____ for using every scrap.

9. Their _____ , heavy clothes were mended many times.

10. A _____ glance at a person's clothing could tell you about the work they did.

11. A _____ wore a leather apron for protection from flying sparks.

12. A peddler often wore a coat with many _____ for carrying small items.

13. Farmers would wear leather _____ that looked like vests.

14. Since all of the colonists' clothing was homemade, each piece

    was _____ .

> **How do you think the children of early settlers felt when they got new clothing?**

Critical Thinking

▶ Write each word from the word bank beside its definition.

1. a search _____

2. to give up _____

3. a unit of volume equal to
   two pints _____

4. to shake or tremble _____

5. a written list of questions
   used for gathering information _____

6. excellence, superiority _____

7. a covering for a bed _____

8. words that are repeated
   or copied _____

9. a female monarch _____

RULE

The letters **qu** stand for the **kw** sound. The letter **k** is silent when it comes before **n**. The letters **kn** can stand for the **n** sound.

queen   **kn**ee

quake	quilt
quality	quit
quart	quotation
quest	queen
questionnaire	

▶ Write the word from the word bank that matches each clue. Then read down to complete the answer to the riddle.

knees	knob	knit	knight	kneel

10. to go down on a bent knee   ☐ _ _ _ _

11. to use long needles to loop yarn together   _ ☐ _ _

12. a rounded handle for opening a door   _ _ ☐ _

13. a soldier in the Middle Ages   _ _ _ ☐ _ _

14. joints of the legs   _ _ _ _ ☐

Riddle: How are ropes tied together in outer space?

Answer: With astro _____ !

Name _____

> Read the sentences. Underline the words in which **ch** stands for the sound you hear in **child.** Circle the words in which **ch** stands for the **k** sound. Mark an X on the words in which **ch** stands for the **sh** sound.

1. You can watch a professional baseball game in many American cities.

2. Some large cities like New York and Chicago have more than one major league baseball team.

3. The fans are a chorus, cheering the teams to victory.

4. At a professional baseball game, you can purchase a brochure with the players' names.

5. In it you can check each player's records of hits and runs.

6. In the game of baseball, pitching is a skill that takes great strength and character.

7. Champion teams have good pitchers to anchor their infield.

8. During a game, the coaches may change pitchers several times.

9. They might, for instance, choose to play a left-handed pitcher against a left-handed batter.

> Complete each sentence with a word from the word bank.

check	reach	chest	coaches
character	catchers	change	attached

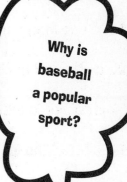

Why is baseball a popular sport?

10. The _____ of each baseball position is different.

11. The manager and _____ decide who will play in the game.

12. The _____ spend most of their time at home plate.

13. They carefully _____ their equipment before each inning.

14. They use a mask and padding to protect their face, _____, and legs.

15. The cage-like mask is _____ by straps to the back of the catcher's head.

16. Fielders sometimes _____ their position during a game.

17. They want to be in the best position to _____ a ball.

Critical Thinking

Lesson 2
The sounds of ch

7

Read the article, and circle each word with the letter c that is followed by a vowel. Then write each word you circled in the correct column. Use each word only once.

A National Favorite

People in America love to eat ice cream. We produce and consume more ice cream than any other country in the world. Americans from the past loved ice cream as much as we do today. George Washington and Thomas Jefferson were no exceptions. Ice cream was served as a dessert course when each man was president. At that time, ice cream was considered a treat reserved for special celebrations because it was so hard to make. Ice needed to be cut from frozen ponds to keep the confection cold.

After the ice cream freezer was invented, ice cream vendors could sell all kinds of new treats. The ice cream cone was invented at the 1904 World's Fair, when a vendor ran out of dishes and placed the ice cream in a rolled up waffle instead. His customers thought that this was an excellent idea, and it remains a popular combination today!

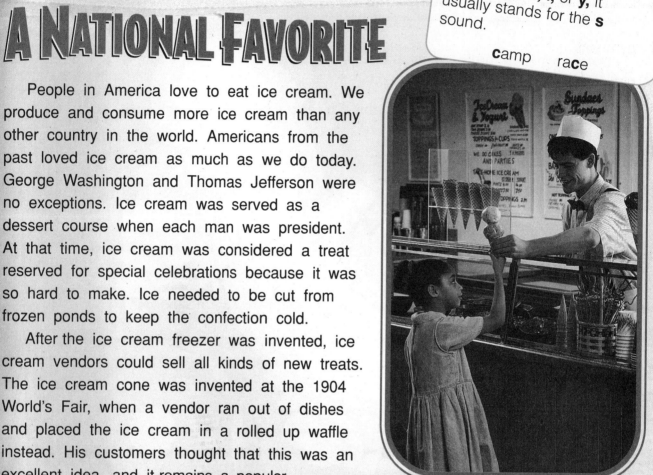

c sounded as k

c sounded as s

Name _____

> Read each word. Write **g** on the line if the word has the hard sound of **g**. Write **j** on the line if the word has the soft sound of **g**.

When the letter **g** is followed by **a, o,** or **u,** it has the hard sound of **g**. When **g** is followed by **e, i,** or **y,** it usually has a soft sound. Soft **g** has a **j** sound.

game   pa**g**e

1. gymnast _____
2. guest _____
3. gazebo _____
4. galloping _____
5. arrangement _____
6. gym _____
7. rage _____
8. sponge _____
9. region _____
10. guess _____
11. age _____
12. tragedy _____

> Use the words from above to solve the crossword puzzle.

Across

4. a disaster or serious event
5. a summerhouse from which a person can gaze at the scenery
6. extreme anger
7. moving very fast
9. an expert in gymnastics
11. number of years a person has lived

Down

1. the way in which something is put together or shown
2. a part of the earth's surface
3. someone who is visiting
8. give an estimate
10. something full of holes, used for cleaning

Circle each word with g in the sentences below. Then write each circled word in the correct column.

1. We changed our plans and decided to travel in August.

2. The regular price of tickets was too much.

3. The travel agent helped us look for bargain rates.

4. The travel agency gave us our tickets.

5. We found our large bags and packed them.

6. Uncle George took us to the airport.

7. At the airport we went to the departure gate.

8. There were many other passengers gathered there.

9. They looked eager and excited to be going on a trip.

10. We sat in the general lounge area and waited to board.

11. We played a game called "It looks like."

12. I said the plane looked like a giant bird.

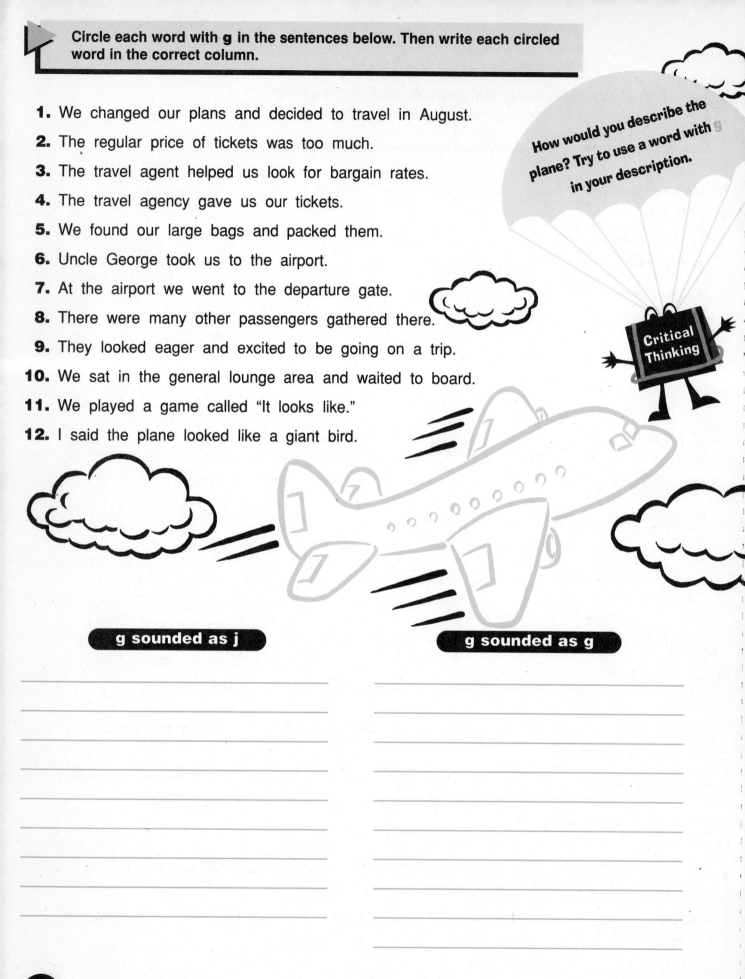

How would you describe the plane? Try to use a word with g in your description.

Critical Thinking

g sounded as j

g sounded as g

Name _____

RULE

The letters **f**, **ff**, or **ph** can stand for the **f** sound.

faster   di**ff**erent   dol**ph**in

1. Aunt Rosa's youngest _____ is coming home.

2. He is a well-known _____ for a weekly magazine.

3. He enjoys working in his _____ .

4. His use of color makes his pictures interesting and _____ .

5. He does his job well in _____ situations.

6. He works hard and has been rewarded many times for his outstanding _____ .

7. He has won _____ and other awards for his photography.

8. Some of his photographs are for sale at very _____ prices.

9. Aunt Rosa is proud of her _____ relative.

affordable

photographer

famous

nephew

efforts

profession

difficult

trophies

beautiful

Read each sentence. Underline the letter or letters that stand for the **f** sound in each word in boldface print. Then circle the answer to each question.

10. The white cat looked like a **phantom** as it crouched in the corner, waiting to leap. What is a **phantom**?

    a wrestler   a moose   a ghost

11. The cat sprang and jumped on the green **philodendron** sitting in the corner. What is a **philodendron**?

    a car   a bureau   a plant

12. The cat **affixed** its claws to the large stalk of the plant. What does **affixed** mean?

    hid   sharpened   attached

13. Later, when the cat got hungry, it **foraged** for food in the kitchen. What does **foraged** mean?

    cried   searched   teased

Say the words in the word bank. Listen to the sound of the letter **s** in each word. Then write the words in the correct columns.

assuring	closure	composers	expression
guess	impression	improvise	leisure
measure	museum	music	observe
pleasure	pressure	sandwich	solo
study	styles	sure	treasure

s	sh	zh	z

Complete the sentences by using words from the word bank above.

1. Jazz is considered the one truly American _____ .

2. This national _____ was developed by African Americans in the early 1900s.

3. Today there are jazz _____ all over the world.

4. Their compositions bring _____ to listeners everywhere.

5. When jazz is performed in a group, each musician has a _____ to play.

6. There are many _____ of jazz, but they all have one thing in common.

7. The musicians _____ , or invent, new parts to every song.

8. So every time you hear a band play a jazz song, you can be _____ it will sound new.

Read the article and circle each word that has the letters wh. Then write those words in the correct columns below. Write each word only once.

The Amazing Whale

Where can you find the largest animal that has ever lived? Some say it's swimming somewhere in the earth's oceans. The blue whale, whose body length can reach about 100 feet (30 meters), can be heavier than an elephant and bigger than the largest prehistoric dinosaur.

When scientists study these huge animals, they find out why they are some of the most fascinating animals found anywhere on earth. For example, while blue whales have excellent hearing, they have small ear openings and no real ears at all on the outside of their bodies. These animals, who live in water, must breathe air to survive. Although a blue whale usually keeps its whole body underwater, it must bring the top of its head to the surface regularly in order to breathe.

wh sounded as h

_____

_____

_____

wh sounded as hw

_____

_____

_____

_____

_____

What is the most interesting or surprising fact you learned from this article?

Critical Thinking

> **Read each sentence. Underline each word in which you hear the sh sound. Then circle the number of the sentence that describes the picture.**

1. Harry Houdini was an accomplished magician who amazed Americans in the early 1900s.

2. Audiences clapped and shouted when his shows finished.

3. Houdini's special talent was escaping from handcuffs and ropes.

4. The audience impatiently waited while Houdini finished untying knots and unlocking locks.

5. An invitation to one of his shows was appreciated by people all over the world.

6. During one show he was locked in a box and pushed into New York Harbor.

> **Find the pair of words that best completes each tongue twister. Write the words on the lines.**

7. Mandy _____ that most _____ make marmalade.

8. Pat Sweet has _____ _____ to pull a pair of pigeons out of her parasol.

9. Alex _____ the artistic acrobat who _____ his act in the air.

appreciated

mentioned

sufficient

accomplished

magicians

patience

Lesson 5
The sounds of sh

14

Name _____

Write each word beside its definition. Then write **thin** or **then** to show what sound **th** has in that word.

| rhythm | marathon | thunder | threat |
| weather | enthusiastic | month | nothing |

Definition	**Word**	**Sound of thin or then**
1. eagerly interested	_____	_____
2. a long race or contest	_____	_____
3. conditions of atmosphere	_____	_____
4. one of 12 parts of the year	_____	_____
5. a loud crash	_____	_____
6. intention to hurt	_____	_____
7. a regular beat	_____	_____
8. not anything	_____	_____

Use a word from above to complete each sentence.

9. People are _____ about the upcoming concert!

10. This is the second concert this _____.

11. A 12-hour _____ of classical music is scheduled.

12. It will be interesting to hear which orchestra has the best _____.

13. The show will go on, even in rainy _____.

14. There is a _____ of severe storms.

15. We have heard some _____ and have seen some lightning.

16. There may be rain, but _____ will stop us from going!

Circle the letters that stand for the sh, wh, and th sounds. Then complete the sentences using words from the word bank.

1. Tina thought she heard a _____ sound in the bushes.

2. She wondered _____ it could be.

3. When she looked, she discovered a _____ little kitten trying to keep warm.

4. Tina _____ softly, and the kitten came over to her.

5. The kitten needed a bath; its fur was _____.

6. Tina wrapped the kitten in her warm, _____ jacket.

7. She didn't know _____ kitten this was.

8. Tina gave the kitten a _____ of food.

9. She _____ gave it some milk.

10. She was very _____ and gentle as she cleaned the kitten.

11. The kitten seemed to be quite _____ but tired.

12. It licked its _____ as it curled up on the floor.

13. Soon all Tina could hear was its gentle _____.

14. Tina got a basket and made a _____ bed for her new friend.

breathing
healthy
then
whispered
dish
whimpering
thick
whiskers
whose
filthy
shivering
special
patient
what

What does this incident tell you about the kind of person Tina is?

Critical Thinking

Lesson 6
Review the sounds of sh, wh, th

Name

 **Reading** ▶ **Read the following article. Then write your answer to the question at the end of the story.**

Birds With a Sense of Humor

Penguins have always fascinated people. Their formal appearance and unique walk make them look cartoonish. Despite their humorous look, these flightless birds are accomplished hunters and swimmers.

Penguins can swim underwater at speeds of 30 miles per hour. This is five times faster than a human Olympic swimming champion! Using an in-and-out-of-the-water technique, these birds can travel long distances, too. The king penguin, for example, can swim underwater for about 25 feet and then "fly" through the air for about 15 feet.

All 18 species of wild penguins live in the southern hemisphere. Although some penguins live in the steamy tropics near the equator, most penguins live in the very coldest regions of the world under severe weather conditions. Their small feet, wings, and heads help them with heat conservation. They also have a thick layer of fat, or blubber, under their feathers to insulate them.

Scientists and photographers who observe these birds know that penguins take enthusiastic pleasure in each other's company and often live in giant flocks of thousands of birds. One reason there are so many penguins is that their only natural enemies are leopard seals and killer whales.

What characteristic of the penguin's body or behavior would you choose to study. Why?

_____
_____
_____
_____
_____

Writing

A scientific study of penguins in Antarctica is about to begin. Your job is to locate scientists, photographers, and guides to join the study. Write a brochure about the trip, using the following helpful hints and words from the word bank to help you.

tricks	questions	watch	treasure	anchor	enthusiastic
guest	passengers	photograph	count	appreciate	place

▶ Learn to survive Arctic weather.

▶ Observe Arctic wildlife.

▶ Research penguin habits.

▶ Learn to communicate with penguins.

Helpful Hints

Review variants, combinations, syllables: Writing

Name _____

Circle each word in which the letters **sc** stand for the **s** sound. Underline each word in which **sc** stands for the **sh** sound. Draw a box around each word in which **sc** stands for the **sk** sound.

RULE

The letters **sc** can stand for the **s, sh,** or **sk** sounds.

science   conscious
scare

1. Scott's friend told Scott about a new science fiction movie.

2. Now, Scott and his brother were waiting in line to see the scary movie.

3. They could smell the scent of popcorn while they waited.

4. Scott and Stan hurried because they could see all the people scurrying toward seats.

5. In the first scene of the movie, a scientist was working in a lab.

6. He had just discovered a new plant formula.

7. The boys were fascinated as the scary plants got bigger and bigger.

8. The scientist scowled when the huge plants suddenly moved toward him.

9. The plants scattered the formula all over the scientist.

10. He turned into a dreadful monster with big muscles and an ugly scar.

11. There was a terrible scuffle while the monster destroyed the horrid plants and finally collapsed!

12. While the monster was unconscious, the formula wore off.

13. At the end, the main character scooped up the formula and destroyed it.

14. Later, Scott and his brother told their parents that the movie didn't scare them at all.

How do you think the boys really felt during the movie? What makes you think that?

Critical Thinking

Read each sentence and look at the word in boldface print. Then use the sentence to figure out the meaning of the word. Fill in the circle beside the best meaning.

1. The **sovereign** who governed the country was wise and fair.
   ○ clown   ○ ruler   ○ traveler

2. The queen's **reign** would last until she died.
   ○ leather strap   ○ special gown   ○ period of rule

3. The queen was a **benign** ruler who was fair and well received.
   ○ kindly   ○ cruel   ○ corrupt

4. The queen started a major **campaign** to improve relationships with other countries.
   ○ a series of actions   ○ a game   ○ a threat

5. Her new **foreign** relations program with other countries was well liked.
   ○ within one's family   ○ inside one's government ○ outside one's country

6. Her loyal advisors **designed** new laws.
   ○ destroyed   ○ thought up   ○ wrote over

7. They presented them for her to **sign**.
   ○ give away   ○ display one's picture   ○ write one's name

8. The queen said she would not **resign** unless she could no longer rule.
   ○ quit   ○ write again   ○ take over

Use a word in boldface print from the exercise above to complete each sentence.

9. The former governor had to _____ from office due to poor health.

10. Journalists covered the new candidate's _____ for election.

11. The candidate's staff _____ her campaign strategy.

12. Newspapers from _____ countries carried stories about it.

13. She wanted to be known as a _____ governor.

14. Her first act would be to _____ an important and popular bill.

15. Then she would meet with the _____ of a nearby country whose _____ had just begun.

Name _____

Read the words below. Underline each word in which rh is used for the r sound. Circle each word in which wr is used for the r sound.

1. rhythm
2. wrote
3. wriggle
4. wrinkled
5. rhinestones
6. rhinoceros
7. wrench
8. rhododendron
9. rheumatism
10. wrong
11. writing
12. wrens
13. wrestle
14. wrap
15. rhapsody

Use a word from above to complete each sentence.

Critical Thinking

Which of the animals described would you have enjoyed seeing at the zoo? Why?

16. The class _____ a thank-you note to the guide at the zoo.

17. Jeff thanked the guide for explaining the habits of the huge _____.

18. Matt enjoyed the _____ that were singing in the bird building.

19. Maria thought a zebra had _____ because it seemed to be limping.

20. All the children liked the _____ skin of the gray elephants.

21. Juan liked the pink flowers on the _____ plants.

22. Eric and Kim enjoyed watching monkeys _____ with each other.

23. Everyone enjoyed watching the snakes _____ and slither in the sand.

24. The teacher agreed that nothing had gone _____ to spoil the day.

25. The teacher mailed the letters after everyone finished _____ them.

careful	dare	aware	care	chair
despair	fair	hair	pair	fare
rare	repaired	shared	stared	repair

1. Carlos _____ at his car for a long time.

2. He was _____ that the car needed to be fixed.

3. He tugged on his _____ while he waited for someone to help him.

4. The mechanic asked Carlos to sit on a _____ .

5. The mechanic told Carlos not to _____ .

6. She said the car could be _____ at the garage.

7. It would need a new _____ of tires.

8. She quoted a price to Carlos that seemed to be _____ .

9. But the car _____ would not be ready until tomorrow.

10. Luckily Carlos had enough money to pay his bus _____ home.

11. Carlos didn't _____ what it cost as long as the car got fixed.

12. A car like his was unusual and _____ .

13. Carlos _____ the car with his brother.

14. He didn't _____ tell his brother about the wreck.

15. Carlos decided to be more _____ in the future.

How do you know that the damage to the car was Carlos's fault?

Critical Thinking

Name _____

> **Write the words from the word bank in the correct column.**

The letters **ear** can stand for the sounds of **ear, ur,** or **air**.

y**ear**   p**ear**l   p**ear**

yearned	heard	appeared	weary	bear
nearby	clear	early	gear	smeared
fear	wearing	searched	tears	

year

_____
_____
_____
_____
_____
_____

pearl

_____
_____
_____

pear

_____
_____

> **Complete the sentences using words from the word bank. Each sentence needs two words.**

1. We _____ that a wild animal had been spotted _____.

2. _____ the next morning we packed our _____.

3. We were _____ warm clothing as we _____ the woods.

4. We became _____ and _____ to rest.

5. Our clothes had rips and _____, and we were _____ with dirt.

6. Just then we saw what _____ to be _____ tracks.

7. When we took a closer look, it became _____ that we had nothing to _____.

Complete the crossword puzzle by writing _ear_ words that fit the definitions.

Across

2. to gain knowledge
5. hair on the face
6. serious and determined
8. a wheel that has teeth that fit into another wheel
10. listen to
11. ornaments for the ears

Down

1. afraid of nothing
3. close by
4. an animal that is one year old
6. wages or money paid to a person
7. a nickname for someone who is much loved
9. tired

24 Lesson 10
Review sounds ear can stand for

Name _____

Complete the sentences using the words in the word bank.

1. The winter _____ blew the leaves off the trees.
2. Darkness made it hard for us to _____ our way.
3. We knew we had to get to the _____ soon.
4. The youngster was _____ and needed help.
5. Although it was raining, we didn't _____ .
6. The wind was just so _____ and strong.
7. What _____ of trouble was the child in?
8. The case _____ me of our last one.

child	mind
wind	wild
find	reminded
blind	kind

Complete the sentences using the words in the word bank.

9. It was rainy and _____ as we searched.
10. We were _____ that the child was in a house.
11. The child was definitely _____ and probably scared.
12. We had to _____ on just a little longer.
13. Suddenly my partner tripped over a wooden _____ .
14. Lo and _____ , the house was right in front of us.
15. We _____ entered the house and found the child safe.
16. We _____ the blanket around the child.
17. We promised that no one would _____ him for getting lost.
18. This was by far our _____ rewarding case.

boldly	most
folded	cold
behold	told
post	lost
hold	scold

Critical Thinking

Who is narrating this story?
What clues led you to this conclusion?

a ghost host	a folder holder	a wild child
a kind mind	sold gold	an old cold

1. What would you call a brain that thinks of ways to help others?

_____

2. What would you call the creature who invites you to a spooky party?

_____

3. What would you call a young person who misbehaves?

_____

4. What would you call precious metal that someone has bought?

_____

5. What would you call a previous illness?

_____

6. What would you call a place to keep papers?

_____

Use words from the word bank to complete the sentences.

find

lost

wind

told

mild

sold

most

cold

gold

blinding

7. Kim wanted to buy a _____ pin for her friend Marge before they were _____ out.

8. The weather had changed from sunny and _____ to snowy and _____ .

9. It was the _____ snow and _____ they had all winter.

10. Kim's mother worried that she might get _____ in the _____ snowstorm.

11. She _____ Kim she would have to _____ another time to go shopping.

Name

 Read the words in the word bank. Write the words in the correct column.

> A syllable is a word or part of a word with a single vowel sound. A word has as many syllables as it has vowel sounds.
>
> **RULE**

knight	phantom	arrangement	threat	music
composer	disappear	dare	grind	numb
wheat	bold	climbing	wholesome	whose
find	unique	questionaire	meanwhile	cashier
declare	innermost	honeycomb	refreshment	overwhelm
difficult	foremost			

One Syllable

Two Syllables

Three Syllables

Read the rules. Then divide the words into syllables by drawing vertical lines.

1. melon

2. facial

3. silent

4. lemon

5. comic

6. repair

7. cabin

8. below

9. declare

10. visit

11. pities

12. modest

13. design

14. nasal

15. music

16. final

17. recent

18. bison

19. finish

20. magic

21. rotate

22. petal

23. pilot

24. punish

25. medal

26. cities

27. radish

28. famous

29. patient

30. lizard

Name

Have you ever read the book *The Wizard of Oz*? In the story a girl named Dorothy and her dog, Toto, are carried from Kansas by a wild tornado to the magical land of Oz. The story is fiction, but the frightening power of a tornado is real.

A tornado, also called a twister or a cyclone, is a funnel-shaped cloud of violently rotating air often formed by an intense thunderstorm. Inside the destructive whirlwind, rotating winds may reach speeds of 200 to 300 miles per hour. The diameter of a tornado can vary from a few feet to a mile. Even though a tornado touches down for less than a few minutes in any one place, it always leaves a path of destruction and despair.

Seasonal weather changes play an important role in forming a tornado. Although they happen year-round, the highest number occur in the spring and early summer. At that time the atmospheric conditions required to form a tornado often come together: thermal instability, high humidity, and the meeting of warm moist air at low levels with the cold dry air from above.

Tornadoes, like hurricanes and earthquakes, are natural disasters over which human beings have no control. Although scientists know much more about tornadoes than ever before, these fierce storms still remind us that the weather can be unpredictable—and very violent.

What do you think is the most frightening part of a tornado?

_____

_____

_____

_____

_____

Writing

You are a reporter for your school newspaper. Yesterday, a tornado touched down in a nearby town. Write a story about the tornado, including an interview with an eyewitness and a local meteorologist. Use the words in the word bank.

Remember the 5 W's!

Who was involved?

What happened?

When did it happen?

Where did it happen?

Why did it happen?

Helpful Hints

appear

careful

despair

find

knowledge

lost

scary

scientist

search

tragedy

wild

Name

Read each word and look at the underlined letters. Fill in the circle beside the letter combination that matches the sound of the underlined letter or letters.

1
ice
- ○ sh
- ○ s
- ○ sk
- ○ z

2
whale
- ○ sh
- ○ h
- ○ w
- ○ hw

3
knead
- ○ k
- ○ s
- ○ n
- ○ f

4
quest
- ○ kw
- ○ g
- ○ j
- ○ hw

5
thick
- ○ s
- ○ ch
- ○ sh
- ○ k

6
game
- ○ g
- ○ j
- ○ ch
- ○ s

7
course
- ○ s
- ○ f
- ○ g
- ○ k

8
gymnast
- ○ g
- ○ j
- ○ s
- ○ ch

9
scent
- ○ s
- ○ k
- ○ sh
- ○ sk

10
whole
- ○ g
- ○ h
- ○ s
- ○ hw

11
music
- ○ z
- ○ s
- ○ zh
- ○ sh

12
magician
- ○ k
- ○ s
- ○ sh
- ○ ck

Read each word and look at the underlined letters. Fill in the circle beside the word that has the same sound.

13
coach
- ○ charm
- ○ orchestra
- ○ technique

14
treasure
- ○ sure
- ○ tense
- ○ leisure

15
because
- ○ hiss
- ○ surprise
- ○ sand

16
scary
- ○ scientist
- ○ conscious
- ○ scour

17
design
- ○ spring
- ○ gnat
- ○ gate

18
wrong
- ○ rope
- ○ wound
- ○ white

Lesson 14
Consonant variants, combinations: Checkup

31

Read the words in the word bank. Then read the story. Write the correct word from the word bank on the line to complete each unfinished sentence. Then answer the questions.

collection	rare	country	museums
region	weather	nearby	science
games	quilts	search	

Visiting _____ is educational as well as enjoyable. There are thousands of fascinating museums in every _____ of our _____ . There are famous art museums with _____ paintings and sculptures from cultures all over the world. There are _____ museums with exhibits about space, electricity, and unusual _____ conditions. There are electronic museums with computer _____ for visitors to play.

Not all museums are giant buildings filled with thousands of items. One tiny museum just shows a _____ of locks and keys. Another shows an arrangement of embroidered _____ that were sewn by hand. If you _____ your own neighborhood or region, you are sure to find an interesting museum _____ .

1. Where can you find museums in the United States?

_____

_____

_____

2. What kinds of exhibits can be shown in science museums?

_____

_____

_____

UNIT 2

Vowel Pairs, Digraphs, Diphthongs, Syllables

There are 13 hidden treasures in this picture. Can you find them?

Dear Family,

In the next few weeks, your child will be learning the different sounds associated with vowel pairs such as ai, ee, and oo, as well as learning about syllables.

At-Home Activities

▶ With your child, find and circle all the hidden pictures in the underwater scene. Take turns making up riddles for all the items.

▶ Encourage your child to research words in newspapers and magazines that rhyme with the hidden picture words and include the same vowel pairs (for example, thread and head or suit and fruit.)

▶ Help your child to create a 3-dimensional underwater scene. Cut out underwater-related pictures from old magazines and catalogs to paste onto posterboard or scrap cardboard. Use clay, sand, and papier-mâché to add texture to the collage.

Book Corner

You and your child might enjoy reading these books together. Look for them in your local library.

Fish in a Flash!
by Jim Arnosky

Learn the basics of spin-fishing outlined in this useful guide.

The Last Voyage of the Misty Day
by Jackie Koller

A teenage girl helps her reclusive elderly neighbor rebuild a boat called the Misty Day.

Sincerely,

_____

Name

Read each sentence. Circle each word that has the long a sound. Then draw a line under the letters that stand for that sound.

1. I do all of my painting in a special studio.

2. The studio is filled with pails, trays, and other containers.

3. The floor is always stained with paint.

4. I often stay in my studio for hours, and sometimes I paint all day.

5. My last painting was a beautiful sailboat on the bay.

6. Today I'm drawing a train whizzing through a field of grain.

7. Later today, Mother and I will pay a visit to a friend.

8. I hope we won't be detained long; I want to finish my drawing today.

9. When time is available, I will paint a picture for my parents' anniversary.

10. Maybe that will help explain to them why I stay in my studio so long!

Circle the word in each row that has the long a sound. Then draw a line under the letters that stand for that sound.

11. tramp	tap	star	tram	stray
12. drab	delay	dance	dash	damp
13. crayon	cancel	clatter	capitol	candle
14. rabbit	ran	ranch	remain	remark
15. matches	mask	mail	marches	mat
16. plain	pals	plant	pans	pats
17. watch	arrest	answer	argue	sway
18. drama	dainty	dam	dad	dare
19. prance	planter	payment	padlock	pantry
20. hatch	half	harvest	hail	hall

train	away	remain	delayed	always	rain
sway	explained	pails	daybreak	repay	stayed
pain	relay	grains	raisin	sailing	sprained

1. We had fun when we were _____ on vacation.

2. We traveled by _____ from our home in Phoenix, Arizona.

3. We were _____ only once during the trip.

4. We _____ at our aunt and uncle's home in California for a week.

5. We wanted to do so many things that we _____ woke up early.

6. One day we even left the house before _____ .

7. Aunt Flo and Uncle George were going to take us _____ on the ocean.

8. Aunt Flo gave us our life jackets and _____ how to use them.

9. We enjoyed it when the boat would _____ back and forth in the breeze.

10. On the shore, we built sand castles with our shovels and _____ .

11. In the evenings, we played games and held _____ races.

12. During one race, Uncle George tripped and _____ his ankle.

13. Uncle George insisted that his injury did not cause him much _____ .

14. The weather was great; it did not _____ once.

15. We thought about how we could _____ Uncle George and Aunt Flo for the good time we had.

16. We baked them several loaves of _____ bread as a thank-you present.

17. We added nuts and three kinds of _____ to the batter.

18. We were sorry that we could not _____ for a longer visit.

What are the most important story events?

Critical Thinking

Name _____

> **Read each word and circle the letters that stand for the long e sound. Then write each word in the correct column below.**

RULE

The vowel pairs **ee** and **ei** can stand for the long **e** sound.

s**ee**   s**ei**ze

agreement	succeed	sleeve	deceive
conceited	beetle	wheelbarrow	teeth
keeper	either	ceiling	receive
Neil	leisure	greenhouse	receipts
seizure	neither	needle	Sheila
sleep	sheet	protein	steeple

see

_____

_____

_____

_____

_____

_____

_____

_____

_____

_____

seize

_____

_____

_____

_____

_____

_____

_____

_____

_____

_____

Read each sentence. Circle each word that has a vowel pair that stands for the long e sound. Then draw a line under the letters that stand for that sound.

1. Sheila Franklin owns and operates a greenhouse in her community.

2. She agreed never to move it from its location on a quiet, secluded street.

3. She enjoys the sight of strong trees, flowering plants, and young seedlings.

4. The sides and ceiling of her greenhouse are glass, which Sheila keeps shiny.

5. Outside, an enormous weeping willow sweeps over the sprawling property.

6. Beside it, a beech tree with gray bark and edible nuts is visible.

7. Sheila gathers honey from beehives that she keeps on her property.

8. She succeeds in her business because she is deeply devoted to her job.

9. One can often see her hauling soil and fertilizer in a large wheelbarrow.

10. She is always ready to seize any chance to improve her business.

11. She works long hours and never seems to get sleepy!

12. Sheila guarantees every plant and shrub that she sells.

13. She reminds her customers to always keep their receipts.

14. Sheila receives many compliments from patrons because she is neither conceited nor deceitful.

15. Everyone agrees that she runs a great business.

16. Even in her leisure time, Sheila is glad to lend a helping hand to anyone.

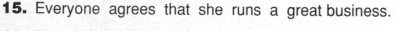

What kind of person is Sheila Franklin? What clues are there in the story that describe her character traits?

Critical Thinking

38 Lesson 16
Vowel pairs ee, ei

Name _____

> **Read each sentence. Circle each word that has the long o sound. Then draw a line under the letters that stand for that sound.**

1. Luis, a person I know, is certain that he will grow taller during the next few years.

2. He boasts that someday he will be as tall as his favorite basketball player.

3. Luis knows that he is the best basketball player on our team.

4. He bounces the ball and stands on tiptoe when he makes free throws.

5. A talented athlete, he shows good sportsmanship wherever he goes.

6. If he misses a shot or commits a foul, Luis never moans or groans.

7. Even when he outscores every other player, Luis does not brag and gloat.

8. He promises never to outgrow his school spirit and always wears our school crest on his coat.

> **Complete each sentence with a word from the word bank.**

9. In our home economics class yesterday, we baked _____ of bread.

10. I forgot my copy of the recipe, so I had to _____ Joan's.

11. We combined the ingredients in large mixing _____.

12. Today, we will _____ the bread and prepare a breakfast.

13. We will serve the toast with _____ eggs and juice.

14. We will poach the eggs in a _____ pan.

15. Mrs. Harris may also let us make _____ or some other cereal.

16. I wonder what we will cook _____.

17. Before the class _____ on to the next unit, we will have a test.

borrow
loaves
shallow
bowls
oatmeal
toast
goes
poached
tomorrow

Twenty-four words in which **oa, oe,** and **ow** stand for the long **o** sound are hidden in the puzzle. Some go across and others go up and down or diagonally. Circle each word as you find it in the puzzle, then write the words in the correct column below.

```
S   C   A   R   E   C   R   O   W   L   A   I   L   O   W
H   F   M   A   N   X   F   O   E   C   L   O   A   C   I
O   I   T   T   H   R   O   W   T   D   O   E   Z   Y   S
W   T   O   C   S   T   P   T   L   M   M   O   A   N   G
B   I   S   R   R   B   E   S   O   B   L   R   G   N   T
T   P   L   O   K   E   T   O   A   D   S   B   O   W   L
O   T   O   W   C   C   A   A   Y   F   A   N   E   Y   B
M   O   A   T   O   E   L   P   J   O   E   F   S   O   A
X   E   N   A   C   U   W   A   N   A   S   O   A   K   O
R   D   R   O   O   X   R   O   T   M   S   H   A   K   O
R   F   E   Z   A   A   T   H   E   L   T   O   A   S   T
T   O   M   O   R   R   O   W   A   S   T   E   T   K   L
```

oa	ow	oe
_____	_____	_____
_____	_____	_____
_____	_____	_____
_____	_____	_____
_____	_____	_____
_____	_____	_____
_____	_____	_____
_____	_____	_____

Use a word from the puzzle to complete each sentence below.

1. After ice skating in the cold, we drank some hot _____ to help us.

2. _____ we will row the boat on the lake.

Lesson 17
Vowels pairs oa, oe; Letter pair ow

Put an X on all the words below with the long **a** sound. Circle the words with the long **e** sound. Underline the words with the short **e** sound, EXCEPT the word that starts with **br.** Write the four words that are left on the lines and choose one word to answer the riddle.

RULE

In a vowel digraph, two vowels together can make a long or short sound or have a special sound all of their own. Vowel digraphs don't follow the long vowel rule. The vowel digraph **ea** can stand for the long **a** sound, the short **e** sound, or the long **e** sound.

break (long a)   leaf (long e)
head (short e)

eat	make	
head	weather	spread
stay	ache	neat
dream	leaf	beach
plea	break	hour
easy	free	great
sail	breath	use
steak	health	threat
noise	daybreak	

1. _____   2. _____

3. _____   4. _____

Riddle

What can you draw
without a pencil
or paints?

A _____ !

Complete each sentence with a word from the word bank. Then write each word you used in the correct column below.

Word Bank:
bleach
break
great
leave
neat
pleasure
reached
ready
steady
steak
thread
underneath

1. "It's my _____ ," I told Jan, "to help you with your laundry."

2. I held the basket as Jan _____ in and removed the clothes.

3. She dropped the clothes into the washing machine and added the soap and _____ .

4. Turning to _____ the laundry room, I saw a sock on the floor.

5. I picked it up and pulled off a loose _____ that hung from the sock.

6. We took a short _____ before we tackled our next chore.

7. Jan held the bucket very _____ as I filled it with hot water.

8. "Are you _____ ?" she asked as I shut off the water.

9. We scrubbed the walls, the floor, and even _____ the cupboards.

10. "This was a _____ day," said Jan.

11. "Everything looks so _____ and tidy."

12. "I think we should go out for a _____ dinner!"

Imagine that you are the narrator. What would you say to Jan's suggestion about dinner?

Critical Thinking

ea as in **break**

ea as in **leaf**

ea as in **head**

Lesson 18
Vowel digraph ea

Name

Read the following journal entry. Circle each word with the vowel digraph ei or ey that stands for the long a sound. Draw a line under the letters that stand for the long a sound.

The vowel digraphs **ei** and **ey** can stand for the long **a** sound.

v**ei**n   th**ey**

September 8, 1878

It's been more than eighteen days since I started on my way to Lambert. Fortunately, I'm not in a hurry, so I've had a chance to go slowly and survey my surroundings. Yesterday I was very excited when I saw what looked liked a vein of silver in some rocks, but it turned out to be quartz glistening in the sun. Later I did see a wonderful sight—two birds of prey, a bald eagle and a red-tailed hawk. They seemed weightless as they floated in the air above me.

With any luck I'll reach Leeville, the neighboring town to Lambert, in two days. I'll know I'm close when I hear the freight-train whistle blow! If I can, I may stop and see the Bridal Veil falls in Leeville—they're supposed to be really neat. Anyway, Petunia is neighing for her dinner, and I've still got to fix the rein I broke today. I'll write again when I reach Lambert.

Read each word listed below. Circle the letters that stand for the long a sound. Then write the number of the word on the line beside its meaning.

1. veil   _____ to hunt other animals

2. prey   _____ to look over carefully

3. rein   _____ a person who lives nearby

4. survey   _____ a sheer piece of cloth

5. neighbor   _____ a strap of leather used to control a horse

Complete each sentence with a word from the word bank.

1. Every _____ the school yearbook staff begins its work.

2. Working _____ hard, the student photographers take pictures.

3. Sometimes they have to be _____ when waiting for good shots.

4. They often take pictures as students _____ for the school play.

5. After the photographs are developed, they are stored in _____.

6. Every year, an _____ is chosen to write an essay for the yearbook.

7. An artistic student is selected to _____ the cover design for the yearbook.

8. When the books are distributed, everyone eagerly collects _____.

9. The students willingly _____ messages in each other's books.

audition
author
autographs
autumn
awfully
cautious
draw
drawers
scrawl

Write the number of each word on the line beside its meaning.

10. shawl _____ a small, round shallow dish

11. cautious _____ to melt; to become unfrozen

12. applaud _____ not graceful; clumsy

13. thaw _____ to express approval by clapping

14. awkward _____ a large pot or kettle

15. saucer _____ to bite, chew, or wear away

16. withdraw _____ to take or pull out

17. gnaw _____ a cloth worn as a covering for the shoulders

18. cauldron _____ to be very careful

Name _____

 Read the definitions. Use the words in the word bank to work the crossword puzzle.

RULE

The vowel digraph **ie** can stand for the long **e** or long **i** sound.

ch**ie**f   t**ie**

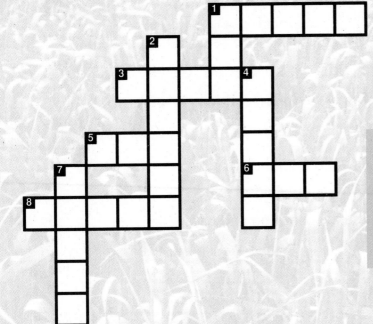

chief	field	lie
niece	pie	shield
thief	tie	yield

Across

1. a person who steals
3. the leader of a group
5. a dessert with a crust and filling
6. something said that is not true
8. to give up; surrender

Down

1. to fasten with string
2. a piece of armor
4. a wide piece of open land
7. the daughter of one's brother or sister

 In each word you wrote above, circle the letters that stand for the vowel sound. Now use some of the words to complete the rule below.

The vowel digraph **ie** can stand for the long _____ sound you hear in the words

_____, _____, _____, and _____.

It can also stand for the long _____ sound you hear in the words _____ and

_____.

Complete each sentence with a word from the word bank.

achieve believed brief disbelief field
niece grief lie pieces relief pies
satisfied shrieked thief tried untie

1. The pet club held its _____ weekly meeting after school.

2. Jason announced that his dog, Trooper, was misbehaving and giving him _____ .

3. Jason explained that Trooper was a _____ because he stole dog treats from a kitchen cabinet.

4. He added, "Trooper always tried to _____ my shoelaces, too!"

5. "He runs away from me when we walk across the grassy _____ ."

6. "I can't even get him to _____ down."

7. Jason's mother wasn't happy with Trooper because he ate one of her prize _____ .

8. The club members _____ with laughter as they imagined Trooper in action.

9. Mr. Andrews, the club sponsor, shook his head in _____ .

10. "How might Jason _____ success in dealing with his dog?" asked Mr. Andrews.

11. Then everybody _____ to offer solutions to Jason's problem.

12. Mr. Andrews's _____ , Elinor, thought Trooper needed more exercise.

13. Annie said she _____ that the dog was seeking attention.

14. Steven suggested that Jason give Trooper small _____ of treats whenever the dog was good.

15. Jason was _____ that he had some ideas to try.

16. With a sigh of _____ , Jason thanked the club members for their help.

What advice would you give Jason in dealing with his dog?

DOG TREATS

Critical Thinking

Lesson 20
Vowel digraph ie

Name _____

Write the correct name for each picture. Then circle the letters that stand for the vowel sound that you hear in that name.

1 	2	3	4 

Read the poem. Circle each word that contains the vowel diagraph oo. Write each word you circled in the correct column below. Use each word only once.

MY DREAM BOOK

Tucked in my bed 'till half past noon,

Reading a book about a hot-air balloon,

Far, far away from my own little room,

Things looked different by the light of the moon.

I flew by an igloo and a herd of moose,

A grove of bamboo, and a lonely goose.

My balloon swooped past mountains steep,

And then it soothed me back to sleep.

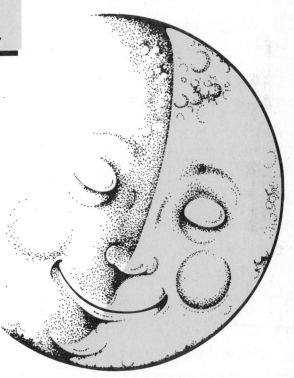

oo as in **boot**

oo as in **cook**

_____   _____   _____

_____   _____   _____

_____   _____   _____

_____   _____   _____

RULE

The vowel digraph **oo** can stand for three different vowel sounds, as in the words **moon, cook,** and **flood.**

1. We are planning our special _____ picnic.

    classroom   foolish   driftwood

2. Tony, our class president, writes our plans in his _____.

    checkbook   notebook   woodwork

3. Ms. O'Rourke announces a _____ plan for the picnic's success.

    flood   foolproof   bookcase

4. She assigns each _____ a special responsibility.

    schoolchild   footprint   bloodhound

5. Someone has to bring the forks and _____.

    books   spoons   pools

6. Everyone will bring some _____.

    stood   fool   food

7. The class decides to have the picnic near the _____.

    book   boot   brook

8. It is located in a beautiful _____ area near the school.

    wooded   barefoot   cooked

9. "All the shady trees will keep us _____," says Tony.

    good   pool   cool

10. It will be easy for our class to _____ to the picnic area.

    troop   hoop   smooth

Do you agree that Ms. O'Rourke's plan is foolproof? Support your answer.

Critical Thinking

Write **i** beside each word that has the same vowel sound you hear in **built**. Write **oo** beside each word that has the same vowel sound you hear in **fruit**.

1. ____ cruise
2. ____ build
3. ____ guilty
4. ____ guitar
5. ____ suit
6. ____ juice
7. ____ building
8. ____ bruise
9. ____ pursuit
10. ____ recruit
11. ____ nuisance
12. ____ biscuits

Complete each sentence with a word from the word bank.

13. The museum has _____ a special room for exhibiting folk art.

14. There is an elaborately carved _____ there, along with several other musical instruments.

15. On the wall there is an unusual painting of a man wearing a two-piece purple _____.

16. One exhibit features carved wooden _____, such as apples and bananas.

17. The museum is hoping to _____ volunteers to conduct tours.

18. I wish that I had some paintings that were _____ to exhibit.

19. Someday there will be a separate _____ just for folk art.

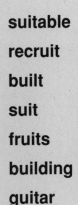

suitable

recruit

built

suit

fruits

building

guitar

1. My parents went on a _____ to
   St. Thomas.
   ○ bruise ○ cruise ○ quilt

2. They stayed in a hotel that had been

   _____ a century ago.
   ○ cruised ○ built ○ recruited

3. Their room in that _____ was simple
   but very comfortable.
   ○ building ○ pursuing ○ cruising

4. During the day their favorite _____
   was taking long walks.
   ○ pursuit ○ recruit ○ cruise

5. The hot Caribbean weather was _____
   for outdoor activities.
   ○ suitable ○ built ○ cruising

6. They walked the crowded streets, often buying

   _____ from sidewalk vendors.
   ○ quilts ○ fruits ○ cruising

7. My mother said the oranges were always

   _____ and sweet.
   ○ juicy ○ guilty ○ recruited

8. She never saw a _____ on a
   banana!
   ○ bruise ○ cruise ○ pursuit

9. They liked to stop at an outdoor restaurant that served
   wonderful _____ .
   ○ suits ○ biscuits ○ quilts

10. My father enjoyed watching street musicians playing

    _____ and steel drums.
    ○ guitars ○ suits ○ cruises

11. They said they felt _____ having so
    much fun without me.
    ○ rebuilt ○ bruised ○ guilty

12. I hope I don't make a _____ of myself
    by asking so many questions about their trip!
    ○ recruit ○ nuisance ○ bruise

What questions would you ask about this trip?

Critical Thinking

Name _____

 **Reading** Read the following article. Then answer the question at the end of the story.

FLYING SYMBOLS

Since ancient times flags have been used to identify tribes, armies, and nations. The first flags might have been cloth streamers tied to poles with carved symbols on top. Eventually the cloth became more rectangular and the symbols were sewn with needle and thread or painted on the cloth.

Flags have flown from chariots, elephants, horses, ships, and military vehicles. Signals of distress or surrender in battle, an upcoming storm, or a special ceremony can also be communicated with flags. For example, the British navy invented a series of code flags in the 1700s and 1800s. By 1889 there was a separate flag for each letter and number. With these flags, complicated messages are still passed from ship to ship today.

National flags frequently include symbols to express important ideas. The flag of Canada, for example, has a maple leaf to represent the red maple trees in that country. The flag of the United States of America has stars to represent the 50 states. The shape of many modern flags is rectangular, but there are exceptions to this rule. The Swiss flag is square, the flag of Quatar is a thin banner, and the flag of Nepal is a pennant shape. Whatever the design, citizens of a country are very loyal to their flag.

What symbol would you choose to decorate your own personal flag? What does it mean to you?

_____

_____

_____

_____

_____

 **Writing**

Your class needs to design a flag to be flown at an all-school field day. Use the following helpful hints and words from the word bank to write a description of your flag.

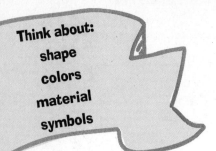

Think about:
shape
colors
material
symbols

plain	crayon	green
either	coat	rainbow
thread	team	great
draw	eight	shield

 **Helpful Hints**

Review vowel pairs, digraphs: Writing

Name _____

> **Complete each sentence with a word from the word bank.**

1. Beth said she would _____ helping with the gardening.

2. Wearing _____ overalls, she walked out to the yard.

3. Beth knelt down to touch the _____.

4. It was still _____ from last night's rain.

5. She noticed that bugs had nearly _____ some flowers.

6. When she saw a large, squirming insect, Beth _____ in disgust.

7. Then she moved her hand swiftly to catch the _____ creature.

8. Beth enjoyed her work and was _____ when it began to rain.

annoying
corduroy
destroyed
disappointed
enjoy
moist
recoiled
soil

> **In the puzzle, circle 12 words containing the diphthongs oi and oy. Then write the words on the lines below.**

```
B  M  I  O  S  T  O  Y
O  L  T  P  O  I  N  T
Y  T  A  M  I  Y  M  S
A  E  N  B  L  U  R  P
L  N  O  I  L  J  E  O
A  J  I  L  M  O  D  I
W  O  S  R  O  Y  A  L
R  I  E  O  I  A  N  E
A  N  A  Y  S  D  T  Z
Z  E  N  O  T  S  M  A
```

_____   _____

_____   _____

_____   _____

_____   _____

_____   _____

_____   _____

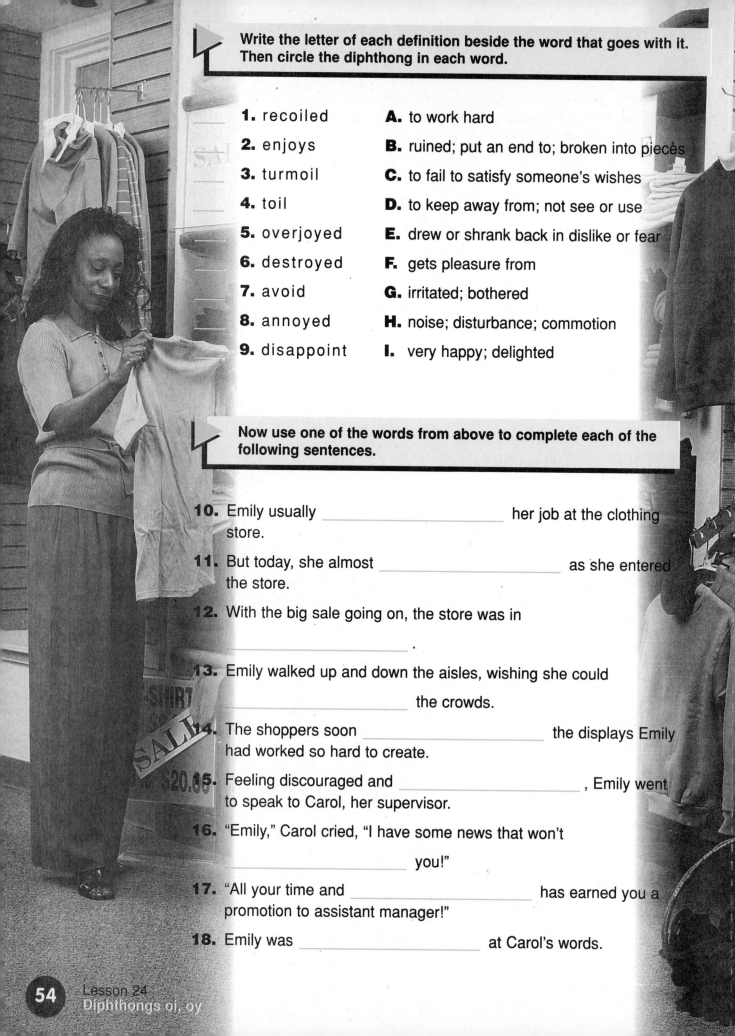

Write the letter of each definition beside the word that goes with it. Then circle the diphthong in each word.

1. recoiled   **A.** to work hard

2. enjoys   **B.** ruined; put an end to; broken into pieces

3. turmoil   **C.** to fail to satisfy someone's wishes

4. toil   **D.** to keep away from; not see or use

5. overjoyed   **E.** drew or shrank back in dislike or fear

6. destroyed   **F.** gets pleasure from

7. avoid   **G.** irritated; bothered

8. annoyed   **H.** noise; disturbance; commotion

9. disappoint   **I.** very happy; delighted

Now use one of the words from above to complete each of the following sentences.

10. Emily usually _____ her job at the clothing store.

11. But today, she almost _____ as she entered the store.

12. With the big sale going on, the store was in _____ .

13. Emily walked up and down the aisles, wishing she could _____ the crowds.

14. The shoppers soon _____ the displays Emily had worked so hard to create.

15. Feeling discouraged and _____ , Emily went to speak to Carol, her supervisor.

16. "Emily," Carol cried, "I have some news that won't _____ you!"

17. "All your time and _____ has earned you a promotion to assistant manager!"

18. Emily was _____ at Carol's words.

Read the words in each row. Circle the words that have the same vowel sound. Then draw a line under the letters that stand for that sound.

The diphthongs **ou** and **ow** often stand for the vowel sound you hear in **loud** and **down**.

1. growl	grunt	ground
2. droop	drowsy	doubtful
3. outbreak	flood	flower
4. funny	power	found
5. counter	prowl	prune
6. unstable	eyebrow	compound
7. mountain	cow	explode
8. scramble	slouch	scowl
9. town	mouth	crawl
10. outweigh	rowdy	rusting
11. account	coward	corner
12. short	shower	shout

Use a phrase from the box to answer each question. Then circle the letters that make the **ou** or **ow** vowel sound in each word.

sound pound	proud crowd	fowl towel
sour power	now chow	brown gown

13. What would you call a cloth to wipe off a chicken? _____

14. What would you call sixteen ounces of noise? _____

15. What would you call the most up-to-date food? _____

16. What slogan could you use to advertise lemons? _____

17. What would you call a dirty dress? _____

18. What would you call a group of very satisfied people? _____

Circle the word that completes each sentence. Write it on the line.

1. The weather was dreary, and it rained _____ the day.

about
throughout
around

2. Dennis and Aimee felt tired and _____.

drowsy
soundly
rowdy

3. In poor spirits, they _____ wearily on the sofa.

pouched
couched
slouched

4. "What can we do to perk up?" Dennis wondered _____.

aloud
about
allow

5. "Let's dress as _____ and have a circus!" said Aimee.

clouds
clowns
cowards

6. Dennis _____ with laughter at the idea.

howled
glowered
growled

7. "I can wear my trick _____ that sprays water," he said.

powder
power
flower

8. "There's that big _____ tie I can wear, too!"

gown
brown
hound

9. "And I'll wear that funny green wig you _____," said Aimee.

round
found
sound

10. She added, "We can paint wide smiles around our _____."

mouths
prows
shouts

Which child will be a
funnier clown? Why?

Critical
Thinking

Name _____

Complete each sentence with a word from the word bank.

anew	crew	outgrew	drew	shrewd
few	jewelry	pewter	jewels	strewn
knew	nephew	renew	newspapers	

1. Ron Richter owns a _____ shop.

2. He is known in town as a _____ businessperson.

3. His _____ , Calvin, works in the store each weekend.

4. Ron also employs a _____ other workers.

5. Ron takes great pride in this dedicated _____ of workers.

6. The shop is filled with gold, silver, and _____ objects.

7. In the front windows, gems and _____ sparkle and shine.

8. Every week the glass cases are filled _____ with gleaming watches, bracelets, and rings.

9. Each Sunday, Ron advertises a sale in all the

   _____ .

10. Last Sunday's advertisement _____ large crowds to the shop.

11. Ron _____ that his business would do well that day.

12. He was so busy that empty boxes were _____ around his office at the end of the day.

13. If business continues to boom, Ron might not

   _____ the lease on his shop.

14. His business already _____ one shop, and he might move again to an even bigger shop.

Why might Ron move his jewelry store to another location?

Critical Thinking

Say each word. Write the number of vowels you see and the number of vowel sounds you hear.

	Vowels Seen	Vowel Sounds Heard			Vowels Seen	Vowel Sounds Heard
1. remainder				24. exhaust		
2. proceed				25. lawbreaker		
3. mountain				26. obey		
4. loafer				27. convey		
5. woeful				28. loaded		
6. abstain				29. lawnmower		
7. retreat				30. greedily		
8. vein				31. receipt		
9. daybreak				32. authentic		
10. laundry				33. roommate		
11. sprawl				34. proof		
12. occupied				35. bounty		
13. toadstool				36. groan		
14. countless				37. misunderstood		
15. likelihood				38. woodpile		
16. fried				39. flaunt		
17. loosen				40. building		
18. spoon				41. wheelbarrow		
19. relieved				42. guilty		
20. yield				43. suited		
21. applied				44. billow		
22. outgrow				45. noise		
23. ounce				46. acquainted		

Name

Watching the Skies

Have you ever wondered about the kinds of flying objects, like comets and asteroids, that fill our solar system? Comets are huge chunks of ice and dust that orbit the sun, leaving a trail of dust behind them. As Earth passes through the dust, tiny particles hit Earth's atmosphere. Most of these particles burn up as streaks of light called meteors. Did you know that the average size of a meteor is about the same as that of a grain of sand?

On the other hand, asteroids are chunks of stone or metal that orbit the sun. Asteroids can be as small as boulders or as large as mountains. In 1994, the space probe *Galileo* traveled past a 35-mile-long asteroid shaped like a potato!

Huge asteroids and comets rarely crash into Earth, but it can happen. Some scientists think a giant asteroid hit Earth about 65 million years ago. Its impact caused enormous turmoil, as rocks vaporized and volcanoes erupted. Because dust and ash blocked the sun, Earth grew cold, and the dinosaurs died.

That was a long time ago. To ensure our safety today, crews of scientists use modern technology to keep a watchful eye on the sky. They are hard at work so that the rest of us can gaze up at the sky to enjoy the celestial views.

How are comets and asteroids different?

Writing

Write an account of your first voyage into outer space. Describe how you would get there and what you expect to see. Use the helpful hints and the words in the word bank to help you.

account	crew	destroyed	disappointed	unspoiled
enjoy	found	jewels	joined	voyage
meteor	shower	mountains	route	planet

How did you travel into space?

What did you take with you?

Who is traveling with you?

When did you leave?

Why are you going?

Helpful Hints

Name _____

Read each word and look at the underlined letters. Fill in the circle beside the word that has the same vowel sound.

1. h<u>ea</u>d	○ red	○ bead	○ neat
2. br<u>ea</u>k	○ make	○ seal	○ breeze
3. l<u>ea</u>f	○ said	○ bread	○ meat
4. th<u>ie</u>f	○ cell	○ pie	○ grief
5. p<u>ie</u>	○ tie	○ slip	○ beach
6. t<u>oo</u>	○ built	○ took	○ boot
7. c<u>oo</u>k	○ suit	○ food	○ took
8. b<u>ui</u>lt	○ cook	○ pie	○ guilty
9. fr<u>ui</u>t	○ suit	○ book	○ pie
10. n<u>ew</u>	○ lie	○ wow	○ few
11. gr<u>ow</u>l	○ boy	○ cow	○ grow
12. j<u>oi</u>n	○ boil	○ shot	○ bid

Read both words and decide if the underlined letters make sounds that are the same or different. Fill in the circle with the correct response.

13. pl<u>ay</u>, <u>ai</u>m	○ same	○ different
14. n<u>ee</u>dle, n<u>ei</u>ther	○ same	○ different
15. m<u>oa</u>n, t<u>oe</u>	○ same	○ different
16. v<u>ei</u>n, <u>ei</u>ther	○ same	○ different
17. <u>au</u>thor, dr<u>aw</u>	○ same	○ different
18. m<u>oo</u>n, c<u>oo</u>k	○ same	○ different

 Read the words in the box. Then read the article and write the correct word from the word bank on the line to complete each sentence.

leisure	brooks	built	cheaper	field	foreign	great
loud	recruited	stayed	succeed	thread	tried	

A WORKING FACTORY

People who lived in the United States during the first half of the 19th century saw a _____ many changes in their way of life. These changes included new machinery to make products like textiles _____ and faster than they could be made by hand. Using giant spools of _____ and huge looms, factories _____ to make cloth quickly to meet demand.

The first textile plant in the United States was _____ on a _____ in Rhode Island, near a river that supplied water power for the machines. Soon it seemed that factories were springing up beside every possible water source, from large _____ to rivers!

Factory work was hard, and working conditions included very few windows and very _____ machinery. Men, women, and children were _____ from local farms and _____ countries to work 18 hours a day, 6 days a week. These workers had no time for _____. Often, they were paid less than two dollars a week! Factory life was hard, but most workers _____ because those jobs were their chance to _____.

1. What was an important change to American life in the mid-1800s?

_____

_____

2. Why do you think children worked in factories?

_____

_____

MEMO

TO: Agent 746
FROM: Central Office
SUBJECT: New Assignment

 NOW; + N'T + P + (TONE – T). PRO +

2 . MID +   + TWEEN 2 BIG .

N + + B + IS A ON A   .

UN +   . COM +   2 O + .

DO PRE + WHAT U F + + ND.

DO MIS + THIS  +  – P:

TO FIND THE TREASURE, RE + A + THE

LETTERS IN W O R D S

> **What is the treasure?**

Which of the coded words did you have the most trouble figuring out? Can you think of a different way to draw that word?

Critical Thinking

Home Letter

Dear Family,

During the next few weeks your child will be learning to identify and use prefixes. Prefixes are word parts that are added to base words and word roots: Un is a prefix, as in unusual; other prefixes include mis, as in misunderstand, sub, as in submarine, and en, as in enrich.

At-Home Activities

Here are some activities you and your child could do together.

▶ Reread the coded message on the other side of this paper, and identify the prefixes in the message.

▶ With your child, create posters with a coded message. You could encode reminders for family members to take the trash outside or not to put an empty jug of milk back in the refrigerator.

▶ Identify the prefixes you see in newspaper headlines, magazine covers, or other printed materials.

Book Corner

You and your child might enjoy reading these books together. Look for them in your local library.

Loads of Codes and Secret Ciphers
by Paul B. Janeczko

Along with the codes and ciphers are historical trivia and information on how to break codes and build simple devices for transmitting secret messages.

From the Mixed-Up Files of Mrs. Basil E. Frankweiler
by E. L. Konigsburg

Two runaways find themselves wrapped up in a mystery about a statue at the New York Metropolitan Museum.

Sincerely,

Circle the answer that best completes each sentence and write it on the line.

1. A base word is a word to which a prefix or suffix

   may be added to change its meaning. **Kind** is the base word

   of **unkindly.** The base word of **unlawful** is _____.

   un   law   ful

2. The base word of **uncover** is _____.

   uncover   un   cover

3. The base word of **replace** is _____.

   re   placed   place

4. A root is a word part to which a prefix or suffix may be added to change its meaning.

   The root of **reduce** is **duce.** The root of **induction** is _____.

   duct   in   ion

5. The root for **relocated** is _____.

   re   loc   ated

6. Roots and base words can have _____.

   roots   prefixes   prefixes and suffixes

7. A prefix is a word part added in front of a root or a base word. **Un** is the prefix of **unhappy.**

   The prefix of **retired** is _____.

   ed   re   tire

8. The prefix of **projection** is _____.

   ject   ion   pro

9. The prefix _____ the meaning of a root or base word.

   changes   doesn't   shortens

10. A suffix is a word part added to the end of a root or base word. The suffix of **worker** is **er.**

    The suffix of **action** is _____.

    act   ion   a

11. The suffix of **contentment** is _____.

    ment   tent   content

List the base word, prefix, and suffix of each word.

	Base Word	Prefix	Suffix
1. unbeatable			
2. overflowing			
3. disagreement			
4. unsuccessful			
5. recounted			
6. semiannually			
7. unwholesome			
8. disappearance			
9. uncomfortable			
10. insightful			

List the root, prefix, and suffix of each word.

	Root	Prefix	Suffix
11. inspecting			
12. exportation			
13. projector			
14. distracted			
15. important			
16. reduction			
17. injected			
18. disposal			
19. transportable			
20. autographed			

Lesson 29
Units of meaning in words

Name

> **Underline the word in each sentence that has a prefix meaning not. Then circle the prefix in that word.**

RULES

Un, dis, ir, in, and im are prefixes that usually mean not.

unhappy = not happy

disapprove = not approve

irregular = not regular

inexpensive = not expensive

impractical = not practical

1. Few people would disagree that General Colin Powell has had a brilliant military career.

2. This undoubtedly was no surprise to his elementary school teachers.

3. As a young man he worked hard to make sure his schoolwork was never incorrect.

4. Colin Powell learned from his parents that nothing is impossible if you work hard.

5. He enrolled in ROTC (Reserve Officers Training Corps) in college and showed unusual leadership ability.

6. In the 1950s many African Americans could not find good jobs because of discrimination.

7. Colin Powell decided that joining the army was his best chance for unlimited career opportunities.

8. After years of hard work, his unflagging dedication earned him the rank of general.

9. General Powell was of indescribable importance to President George Bush as the Chairman of the Joint Chiefs of Staff.

> **Find the 12 words with the prefixes un, dis, ir, in, im hidden in the word puzzle. Use the word bank to help you.**

```
I  U  I  N  V  A  L  I  D  I
R  I  N  D  I  R  E  C  T  N
R  A  B  D  C  M  D  E  F  S
E  G  H  I  O  D  P  J  K  I
G  U  L  S  M  I  N  U  O  N
U  N  L  O  O  S  E  P  R  C
L  C  Q  B  R  O  S  T  U  E
A  A  V  E  W  W  X  Y  Z  R
R  P  I  Y  U  N  M  A  K  E
I  M  P  E  R  F  E  C  T  M
```

disobey	disown	imperfect
impure	indirect	insincere
invalid	irregular	uncap
undo	unloose	unmake

Add a prefix from the soccer ball to each base word. Write the new word on the line.

un   dis
ir   in
im

1. Tammy's soccer team has won every game and seems to be

_____ this year.
   (beatable)

2. There has been _____ improvement
   (credible)

since last season.

3. Last year there were many _____.
   (advantages)

4. Practice was held at a time that was _____ for the players.
   (convenient)

5. Coach Lawson was very busy and her directions were _____.
   (clear)

6. Players were often _____ what to do.
   (certain)

7. Because of their poor record, the players were

_____ at practice.
   (attentive)

8. Some players acted in a very _____ way.
   (mature)

9. They were _____ and inconsiderate.
   (responsible)

10. No one is _____
    (happy)

with the way this year's season is progressing.

11. Coach Lawson won't look for any new players

next season because she thinks they are all

_____.
   (replaceable)

12. She believes that it is _____
    (possible)

to have a better team!

Name _____

Fill in the circle beside the word that completes each sentence. Write the word on the line.

1. Our class just completed a bulletin-board display for the school,

_____ "Save Our Environment."

- ○ entangled
- ○ entitled
- ○ enlarged

2. We _____ pictures of various endangered animals.

- ○ included
- ○ intended
- ○ invented

3. Most of the _____ was gathered from the Internet.

- ○ independence
- ○ information
- ○ inscription

4. We found out that there are hundreds of _____ birds, plants, and animals.

- ○ entangled
- ○ enriched
- ○ endangered

5. Our goal was to _____ younger students to begin thinking about the environment.

- ○ encourage
- ○ enrich
- ○ enlarge

6. People need to be reminded that they _____ this earth with millions of other species.

- ○ inhabit
- ○ inhale
- ○ include

7. Many organizations help us _____ our knowledge of animals that are at risk.

- ○ income
- ○ increase
- ○ indoors

Critical Thinking

Do you think it is important to know about endangered species and to help solve the problem? Give reasons for your answer.

Write the letter of the phrase that tells the meaning of the word.

_____ **1.** entangled   **a.** put in a cage

_____ **2.** inhale   **b.** breathe in

_____ **3.** enchain   **c.** live in or on

_____ **4.** enrobe   **d.** write on stone or paper

_____ **5.** inhabit   **e.** fasten something in place with a chain

_____ **6.** inscribe   **f.** get twisted up or caught in

_____ **7.** encage   **g.** add to or grow

_____ **8.** increase   **h.** dress in a long, loose garment

Look closely at the pictures and read their names. Then use the names to answer the questions.

king

cat

lion

bike

tire

bracelet

9. Which one is being _inflated_?

_____

10. Which one is _encaged_?

_____

11. Which one is _enrobed_?

_____

12. Which one is _enchained_?

_____

13. Which one is _entangled_?

_____

14. Which one is being _inscribed_?

_____

70   Lesson 31
Prefixes in-, en-

Name _____

▸ **Circle each word below in which mis or mal is used as a prefix.**

mismatch	maladjusted	mistrusts	mister
missile	mail	malformed	mistake
misty	mallet	mistreated	malnutrition
malnourished	misfortune	misled	miscalculated

> **RULE**
>
> **Mis** and **mal** are prefixes that usually mean *bad* or *badly*.
>
> **mis**behave = behave badly
>
> **mal**treat = treat badly

▸ **Use one of the words circled to complete each sentence. Write the word on the line.**

1. Samson, the wildcat, had the _____ of being captured.

2. He _____ his own strength.

3. He was _____ into thinking he could run so fast he'd never get caught.

4. However, because Samson's front paw was _____, he could not move quickly.

5. He made the _____ of being overconfident.

6. After his capture the biologists noticed that Samson was thin and suffered from _____.

7. They took him to the zoo, where he would not be _____ by people.

8. At the zoo, Samson adjusted so well to the other animals that no one could say he was _____.

9. Samson now gets plenty of food and is no longer _____.

10. People have become his friends, and Samson no longer _____ anyone.

> How do you think Samson's capture affected his life?

Critical Thinking

Use the word in boldface print to replace two or more words in each sentence. Write each new sentence on the lines.

1. misfortune   We had bad luck on our camping trip.

_____

_____

2. misled   Our guide, Miles, was inexperienced, and we were led astray.

_____

_____

3. misread   Miles incorrectly read the map, and we took a wrong turn.

_____

_____

4. miscalculated   Then he incorrectly calculated the distance back to our starting point.

_____

_____

5. misinformed   We were unhappy that we had been given wrong information.

_____

_____

6. misbehaved   Some members of our group behaved badly and had to be reprimanded.

_____

_____

7. maladjusted   Others were badly adjusted to life outdoors.

_____

_____

8. malnutrition   Fortunately we were found before we began to suffer from a lack of good food.

_____

_____

If the guide had been experienced, how would the camping trip have been different?

Critical Thinking

Lesson 32
Prefixes mis-, mal-

Name _____

> **Read each definition below. Choose a word from the word bank that fits the definition and write the word on the line.**

produce	predict	promoted	proceed
prejudge	prospective	premature	preconceived

1. _____ put forward in rank

2. _____ formed in one's mind ahead of time

3. _____ decide in advance before enough is known to judge fairly

4. _____ to bring forth

5. _____ to tell what one thinks will happen in the future

6. _____ expected or likely

7. _____ to move along

8. _____ too hasty or too early

> **Use a word from the word bank to complete each sentence.**

9. Dan's mother was just _____ to a better job.

10. She interviews _____ employees for the company.

11. It is difficult to _____ which person will do the best job.

12. Mrs. Gale does not _____ those she interviews.

13. She tries not to have _____ ideas about people.

14. She takes her time and never makes _____ decisions.

15. When the interview is over, Mrs. Gale helps the person to _____ to the next step.

16. Mrs. Gale's careful decisions _____ happy employees.

▶ **Circle each word in which pre or pro is used as a prefix.**

prepaid	prohibited	prepared	prolong
pretty	problem	precocious	preoccupied
prospective	premature	protested	prowl
proclaimed	procrastinated	precious	proposed

▶ **Write a word you circled to complete each sentence. Use each word only once.**

1. Dad _____ a wonderful idea.

2. He suggested that we _____ our vacation and stay another day.

3. No one _____ when Dad brought up the idea.

4. However, our decision was _____ .

5. We had _____ too long.

6. The hotel was full, so we were _____ from staying.

7. We were disappointed as we _____ to leave.

8. We wished that we had _____ for our room.

9. Dad _____ that we would plan more carefully next year.

10. We hope that our _____ vacation will have a happier ending!

What do you think the family decided to do next?

Critical Thinking

Name

 **Reading** ▶ **Read the following "Nothing Is Impossible" column. Then write your answer to the question.**

 # NOTHING IS IMPOSSIBLE

Help! My parents misunderstand me. I have friends, but I like spending time alone outside. Is that unhealthy? My folks think I should join a club or play sports. I dislike sports except for fun. I'm not unsociable. How can I enlighten them?

—Uncertain Ned

Dear Uncertain:
You sound fine to me. Many people spend lots of time with groups of people. But your folks aren't entirely misguided. Group activities help us share our interests. Try a club that meets once a month instead of every week—and meets outside—or help out at an animal shelter. You could give

encouragement to animals who need homes. Just remember, nothing is impossible.

It's irrational! My older sister went to this school too, and my teacher mistakes me for her all the time. I don't like to disobey him, but it angers me not to be called by my own name.

—Discouraged Dina

Dear Discouraged:
I'd be discouraged, too. Tell him how you feel, then make a bright name tag and wear it for a few days to remind him. It might help immeasurably. Remember, nothing is impossible. And remember too, we're all a little imperfect–even me!

How would you rate the suggestions the "Nothing Is Impossible" writer gave Ned and Dina? What do you like and don't like?

_____

_____

_____

_____

_____

_____

Writing

The "Nothing Is Impossible" editor needs help. Write answers to these two letters. Use the helpful hints and words from the word bank.

discourage	entitle	
impatient	impossible	
insightful	inspire	
irresistible	maladjusted	misinformed
preconceived	promote	unusual

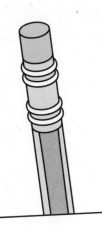

- Respect the letter writers!

- What would you do in the same situation?

- Help and encourage your friends.

- Remember how other people have helped you.

Helpful Hints

How can I help? My brother is in third grade. He's not insecure but he is shy. It's hard for him to try new things. —Jack

_____
_____
_____
_____
_____
_____

What can we do? We want to start a school newspaper. Our teacher last year said it would take too much time. Will it? What if our new teacher says the same thing? We know we should start small. —Brownville Fifth Grade

_____
_____
_____
_____
_____
_____

Name

▶ **Find the twelve words with the prefix re or ex in the puzzle. The words appear horizontally, vertically, and diagonally. Use the word bank to help you.**

RULES

Re is a prefix that means *again* or *back*. **Ex** is a prefix that means *out of* or *from.*

rewrite = to write again

return = to go back to

export = to send goods out of or from a country

```
E Q R E C A L L X C D S E P
X X E E C R E F L E C T T R
C M C W T E F M E Y T A E E
L Q I U E R G E H R B A X C
A E T W S Q A X E E L A C O
I X E D P E X C H A N G E N
M H B K H X M I E P S V E S
Q A C R E H O T S P R J D T
W V Z L K A B E R E C T I R
R S T A R U L I V A P B T U
D T L N G S B R G R H K E C
T A E X C T A E X C E R P T
```

exceed	**excerpt**	**exchange**
exclaim	**excuse**	**exhaust**
reappear	**recall**	**recite**
reconstruct	**reflect**	**retrace**

▶ **Use one of the words you circled above to match each definition below. Write the word on the line beside its definition.**

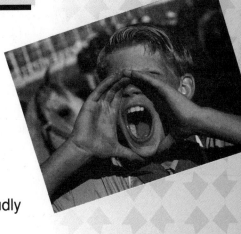

1. _____ to forgive

2. _____ to use up the strength of

3. _____ to go back over

4. _____ to go beyond

5. _____ to remember from the past

6. _____ to cry or speak out suddenly and loudly

7. _____ a part from a book, play, or speech

8. _____ to repeat or say over again from memory

9. _____ to give up one thing for another

10. _____ to show up again

11. _____ to build over

12. _____ to give back a picture

© MCP All rights reserved. Copying strictly prohibited.

Lesson 35
Prefixes re-, ex-

77

▶ **Circle each word in which re or ex is used as a prefix.**

reassure	exciting	really	relocate
reading	explain	expect	reach
rewash	reprint	reason	expressed
ready	replaced	rearrange	reflected
retrace	recreate	exchange	recalled

▶ **Write a word you circled to complete each sentence. Use each word only once.**

1. Amanda was thrilled when she learned that her family had to _____ to a new state.

2. Amanda was not sure what to _____ in her new home.

3. But she anticipated many _____ adventures.

4. Amanda _____ the last time she had moved.

5. She was eager to make new friends, but knew that her other friends could not be _____ .

6. Amanda's sister _____ concern and anger about the move.

7. Her unhappiness was _____ in her face.

8. Amanda tried to _____ why she was so delighted.

9. She tried to _____ her sister that things would work out.

10. Amanda reminded her sister that they could _____ letters from their old friends.

Why do you think Amanda's sister is concerned about moving?

Critical Thinking

Lesson 35
Prefixes re-, ex-

Name _____

> **Write the letter of each word on the line beside its definition.**

RULES

Fore is a prefix that means *front* or *before*. **Post** is a prefix that means *after*.

forehead = front of the head

postscript = message written after the signature of a letter

____ **1.** A time before midday

____ **2.** Put off until later

____ **3.** An ability to see ahead and know about something before it happens

____ **4.** First in importance

____ **5.** A message added after the signature of a letter

____ **6.** To predict what is coming before it happens

____ **7.** Generations after us; people of the future

a. postscript

b. foresight

c. posterity

d. postpone

e. forenoon

f. forecast

g. foremost

> **Write a word from the list above to complete each sentence.**

8. Our class wrote letters to save for

_____.

9. We planned to seal them in a time capsule

in the _____ on Friday.

10. The idea of describing our present lives was

_____ in our minds.

11. We also wanted to _____ what would happen in the future.

12. Mark didn't use _____ in planning his time wisely.

13. He was adding a _____ to his letter as the clock struck 12.

14. We were disappointed when our teacher said we had to _____ the project until Monday.

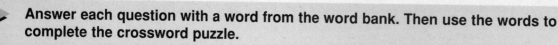

Answer each question with a word from the word bank. Then use the words to complete the crossword puzzle.

postpone	foresee	forepaws	postscript	postwar
forenoon	forecast	forehand	foreman	posterity
	forehead	foretaste	forewarn	

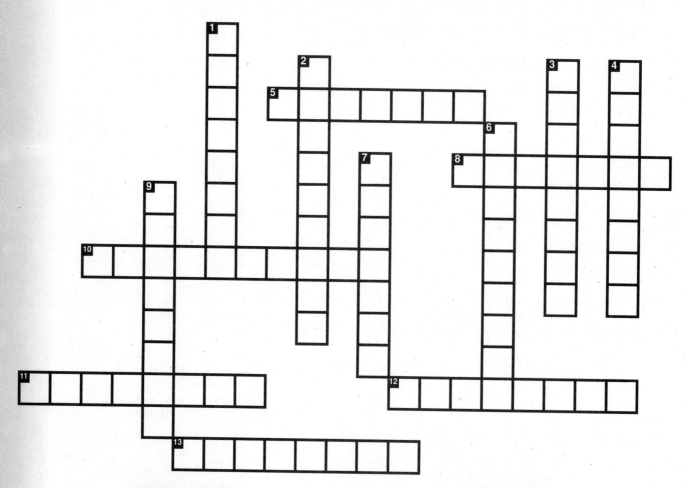

Across

5. What is the person in charge of a work crew called?

8. What does a prophet supposedly do with the future

10. What do the letters *P.S.* at the end of a letter stand for?

11. What period of the day is 11 o'clock in the morning?

12. What is the name of a type of stroke used in tennis?

13. What means "to caution in advance"?

Down

1. What are the front feet of an animal called?

2. Who are the generations that live after us?

3. What does a weather person do?

4. What do hair bangs cover?

6. What is a sample of what is to come?

7. What do you call the period of time after war?

9. Which word means "put off an event until a later date"?

Name _____

RULE

When **over** is used as a prefix, it means *too* or *too much*. If an adjective begins with **over**, it usually means *too*. If a verb begins with **over**, the prefix usually means *too much*.

overeager = too eager

overspend = to spend too much

overdo	overtired	overcrowded
overconfident	overflowed	overpriced
overgenerous	overheard	overspent
overview	oversweet	

1. The packed gymnasium was _____ the night of the big game.

2. Some of the crowd even _____ into the hallway.

3. The vendors had _____ their popcorn and hot dogs.

4. Some of the soft drinks were _____ and warm.

5. However, the fans didn't seem to mind if they _____ for snacks.

6. The players knew they could win but were not _____.

7. They warmed up but were careful not to _____.

8. They had trained long and hard and hoped not to become _____.

9. After the victory the sports announcers were _____ with their praise.

10. They gave their listeners an exciting _____ of the game.

11. We even _____ one announcer calling it the game of the century!

Do you wish you had seen the basketball game? Why?

Critical Thinking

1. Mr. Taylor was _____ when he opened his new restaurant.

   ○ overprotect   ○ overconfident   ○ overdone

2. It was located in an _____ area, so he anticipated a great deal of business.

   ○ overeat   ○ overcharge   ○ overpopulated

3. On the day of the grand opening, the restaurant was _____.

   ○ overcrowded   ○ overflow   ○ overeager

4. It was very warm, and many of the customers became _____.

   ○ overhead   ○ overheated   ○ overage

5. The hostess was _____ and annoyed some of the patrons.

   ○ overtalkative   ○ overhear   ○ overthrown

6. The waitresses were _____ taking care of so many customers.

   ○ overspent   ○ overworked   ○ overbalanced

7. Much of the food was _____ and unappetizing.

   ○ overthrow   ○ overcooked   ○ oversee

8. The customers couldn't finish their orders because the portions were _____.

   ○ overlay   ○ overgenerous   ○ oversleep

9. People felt the meals were _____ and were disappointed with Mr. Taylor's new establishment.

   ○ overtook   ○ overwork   ○ overpriced

10. Some customers stopped coming, so the restaurant was _____ with food.

    ○ overhang   ○ overtake   ○ overstocked

11. Mr. Taylor was discouraged when he _____ so many complaints.

    ○ overload   ○ overheard   ○ overcast

12. He _____ and talked about closing the restaurant.

    ○ overdo   ○ overreacted   ○ overcharge

What advice would you give Mr. Taylor?

Critical Thinking

Name _____

 Use the words from the word bank to complete each sentence. Use each word only once.

RULE

The prefixes **co, com,** and **con** mean *with* or *together.*

coauthor = someone who works with others

combine = to join together

conspire = to plan something secretly with others

1. The school principal asked our class to find a way to help _____ the trash problem at school.

2. She had already asked the school to _____ paper by using both sides.

3. We formed a _____ to brainstorm ways to recycle paper and cardboard.

4. Two students and our teacher had a _____ with representatives from the town.

5. The two _____ of the recycling department were very helpful.

6. Now, all the classrooms _____ recycle over 20 pounds of paper and cardboard a week!

conquer combined
committee
codirectors
conserve
conversation

One word from the word bank is hidden on each line. Circle one letter of each pair to spell it. Then find eight animal names by reading down the letters you did not circle. Write each name on a line below.

CM	OS	TN	SW	EM	OR	VS	ER
OC	HO	MI	BH	OI	NT	NE	DO
CO	OE	AG	AU	TU	TH	AO	BR
SC	OE	EM	LP	SE	ET	EK	DI
CE	PO	NR	QE	EU	ER	ER	NS

conserve   competed
conquers   coauthor
combined

_____ _____ _____ _____
_____ _____ _____ _____

Choose a word from the box that completes each sentence and write it on the line. Use each word only once.

comanagers	consisted	committee	consequently
competitive	convinced	consented	comfortably
cooperate	combination	conversation	contributed

1. Brian is very _____ .

2. He finds it difficult to

   _____ with others.

3. _____ , he does not
   work well with others.

4. Once Brian was asked to head a

   _____ at school.

How would you describe Brian's friend's personality?

Critical Thinking

5. The group _____ of eight of his classmates.

6. There was very little _____ at the quiet meetings.

7. Brian _____ his best friend to join the committee.

8. His friend _____ after much persuasion.

9. The two boys worked as _____ of the group.

10. They made a great _____ !

11. Because of their personalities, they each _____ different talents.

12. The members then were able to work together _____ .

Prefixes co-, com-, con-

Name _____

RULES

Sub can mean *under, below,* or *not quite.* **Mid** can mean the *middle part.*

subway = underground way or passage

midnight = middle part of the night

1. a ship that goes under sea: _____ marine

2. halfway; in the middle: _____ way

3. a person below another in rank: _____ ordinate

4. put down or overcome by superior force; conquer: _____ due

5. air above the ground; in the middle of the air: _____ air

6. existing below the conscious; not fully recognized in the mind: _____ conscious

7. middle of the week; Wednesday: _____ week

8. middle of a stream: _____ stream

▷ **Follow the directions to finish the picture below.**

9. Draw a **submarine** in **midocean.**
10. Draw a jogger who is **midway** over the bridge.
11. Draw a large fish in **midstream.**
12. Draw an airplane in **midair.**

Answer each question by circling the correct answer.

1. Which day occurs **midweek?**

Sunday   Friday   Wednesday

2. Which animal would you look for in **midstream?**

robin   mouse   fish

3. Which of these travels **underwater?**

ship   submarine   subway train

4. When is **midday?**

noon   10 A.M.   2 P.M.

5. Which one is in a body's **midriff** area?

leg   neck   waistline

6. Which one is an **underground railroad?**

subsoil   subset   subway

7. When is **midnight?**

12 o'clock at night   10 o'clock at night   6 o'clock at night

8. Which word means the opposite of **subtract?**

divide   add   multiply

9. What happens to a storm that **subsides?**

It dies down.   It causes damage.   It comes back again.

10. What is an **undercover investigation?**

one done inside   one done in secret   one done alone

11. Where is the **midpoint?**

the beginning   the middle   the end

12. Which word means "**to go underwater**"?

submerge   subtract   subscribe

Name

Choose the word from the word bank that describes each picture, and write it on the line.

RULES

The prefixes **bi** and **tri** indicate number. The prefix **bi** means *two*. **Tri** means *three*.

bicycle = a vehicle with two wheels

tripod = a stand with three legs

bifocals	biceps	triplets	biplane
triangle	trio	tripod	binoculars

1

_____

2

_____

3

_____

4

_____

5

_____

6

_____

7

_____

8

_____

Use each of these words from the list in a sentence of your own.

9. bifocals _____

10. triangle _____

11. binoculars _____

12. triplets _____

13. trio _____

binoculars   triplets

bicentennial   tricycles

tricolored   bifocals

tricentennial

The U.S. Bicentennial

On July 4, 1976, the people of the United States celebrated the two-hundredth anniversary, or _____ , of the signing of the Declaration of Independence. For months before the big day, people splashed red, white, and blue paint all over America. Some children painted each wheel of their _____ with one of the three patriotic colors. On the day itself, one set of _____ paraded in New York, each one dressed in one of the flag colors. One man even sported a _____ beard! The original Declaration of Independence was displayed in Washington, D.C. The lines of people waiting to see it were so long that some people used _____ to view the document from a distance. Those who got close did not need to wear _____ to read the bold signature of John Hancock!

In 2076, America will celebrate its _____ . How old will you be?

Do you think big celebrations like this one are important? Why or why not?

Circle each word in which **bi** or **tri** is used as a prefix.

bimonthly	triangle	bilingual	binoculars	trillion
biceps	trickle	billboard	bifocal	bias
tribute	trivia	trilogy	bitter	tripod
triceps	tricycle	biplane	bicycle	bicker

Critical Thinking

Name _____

He's a Tiger!

On April 13, 1997, an extraordinary young man put on his new green blazer—the symbol of the U.S. Masters Golf Champion. At age 21, golfer Tiger Woods became not only the youngest Masters champion, but the first person of color to win that prestigious title.

Setting new records isn't a new achievement for Tiger, though. As an amateur golfer, he was U.S. Amateur Golf Champion an unprecedented 3 times, breaking the record of golf great Jack Nicklaus. Tiger was also the youngest person to ever win that title.

Tiger's dedication, insight into the game, and his ability to predict where the ball is going before he swings the club are some of the keys to his success. The young golfer's concentration is legendary—nothing distracts him and he rarely miscalculates a shot. But that doesn't make him overconfident because Tiger comes prepared to play—and win!

Eldrick "Tiger" Woods knew how to swing a golf club before he could walk. By the time he was ten, Tiger was unbeatable on the golf course, and destined to be a champion. "Expect the best but prepare for the worst," his parents told him. It is commendable advice, and that's what Tiger has done.

What do you think "Expect the best but prepare for the worst" means? How would this advice help a young person?

_____

_____

_____

_____

_____

_____

_____

Writing

Not everyone has Tiger Woods' abilities, but playing just for fun can be fun! Use the helpful hints and five words from the word bank to write a recruiting poster for an after-school sports club.

biceps	combination	compete	postpone
confidence	exciting	expect	reassure
foremost	midweek	overworked	recognize

Sports are fun.

Meet new friends.

Get some exercise.

Practice new skills.

Learn about teamwork.

Helpful Hints

Review word parts and prefixes: Writing

Fill in the circle beside the answer that best completes each sentence.

1. In the word *uncovered, cover* is the _____.

○ suffix
○ base word
○ prefix

2. In the word *discomfort, dis* is the _____.

○ suffix
○ base word
○ prefix

3. In the word *unpolished, ed* is the _____.

○ suffix
○ base word
○ prefix

4. In the word *misbehaved, mis* is the _____.

○ suffix
○ base word
○ prefix

5. In the word *overworked, work* is the _____.

○ suffix
○ base word
○ prefix

6. The _____ of a new comet thrilled the astronomers.

○ mistake
○ discovery
○ discard

7. The deer was so _____ it could barely walk.

○ malnourished
○ misinformed
○ disorganized

8. Our plan to make all our own costumes turned out to be _____.

○ entitled
○ inedible
○ impractical

9. That _____ dance performance could never be repeated.

○ unforgettable
○ irresponsible
○ inscription

10. The members of the food _____ decided to serve soup and salads.

○ combination
○ committee
○ foremost

Read the words in the box. Then read the story. Write the correct word from the box on the line to complete each unfinished sentence. Then answer the questions.

biplane	discovers	displayed	inspired	posterity	unforgettable
irregular	midway	mistake	overpriced	prohibited	unusual

Collecting Stamps

Stamp collecting is popular all over the world. A novice collector quickly

_____ that stamps from around the world can be purchased for a few

cents each. A stamp collection can become an historical record for _____

by showing examples of a country's art and important people.

Presidents and hundreds of Americans have _____ the portraits on

U.S. stamps. Pictures of living women and men, however, are _____ from

being _____ on stamps.

What makes certain stamps valuable? Their rarity! Such stamps usually have something

_____ about them. One of the most famous rare stamps, a 1918 United

States 24-cent stamp, featured a _____ _____ on

the stamp. One hundred stamps were printed with the plane upside down before the

_____ was noticed! Four of these stamps sold for one million dollars in

1989. You might think that amount is _____ for postage stamps, but what

if you found the next rare stamp? Then you would have the _____

experience of adding a rare and _____ stamp to your collection!

1. What are some of the reasons people collect stamps?

_____

_____

2. What irregularity appeared on the 1918 issue of a 24-cent-stamp?

_____

_____

Roots, Compounds, Possessives, Contractions, Syllables

At the Science Fair

We rushed into the science fair,
We couldn't wait at all,
To see the kinds of projects made
From stuff bought at the mall.

We looked about for projects
that each of us submitted,
After all the work we did
It was time to see who'd win it!

There was a tree with pointed leaves,
That I grew from a nut.
And Betty Jones's frog display,
I suspect will make first cut!

We inspected tiny specimens;
A volcano spouting steam.
But my friend's video on molds
Was the weirdest thing I've seen!

Then we saw Zack's earthquake,
Made from wire and clay,
A motor produced vibrations—
And it won first prize today!

What kinds of projects have you produced for the science fair?

Critical
Thinking

1ST

Home Letter

Dear Family,

In the upcoming weeks your child will be exploring the roots of words, compound words, possessives, and contractions. We'll also continue to learn about syllables.

At-Home Activities

▶ Look at the poem on the other side of this letter with your child. See if he or she can find words containing the roots mit, ject, duct, spec, spect (submitted, project, product, specimens, inspected). See if your child can also find compound words, contractions, and possessives.

▶ Help your child make a list of science experiments and projects he or she has done or has seen somewhere (including on TV science shows). Which experiment interests your child most? Ask why.

▶ Encourage your child to research places to visit in your local area where science is a focus. Such places include museums, state, local, or national parks and nature preserves. Then plan a day there with your child to promote science!

Book Corner

You and your child might enjoy reading these books together. Look for them in your local library.

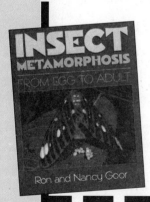

Insect Metamorphosis
by Ron and Nancy Goor

Learn about the developmental stages of many common insects.

A Young Person's Guide to Science
by Roy A. Gallant

Explore scientific theories and innovations in this authoritative text.

Sincerely,

_____

Name _____

 Read the sentences and underline the words that contain the roots pos, pel, or pul.

> **DEFINITIONS**
>
> A **root** is a word part to which a prefix or suffix may be added to change its meaning. **Pos** usually means *put* or *place*. **Pel** or **pul** usually means *push* or *drive*.
>
> **pos**ition = the way in which a person or thing is placed or arranged
>
> pro**pel** = to push or drive forward

1. Our gym teacher proposed that our class complete a ropes course.

2. I was nervous, but I was positively sure I wanted to go.

3. My pulse raced when I first saw the ropes course.

4. I stared at the steel cables and ropes and tried to dispel my fear.

5. For safety we were compelled to wear helmets and harnesses.

6. The mosquitoes made me wish I'd remembered insect repellent.

7. I cheered my best friend as she got into position to start the course.

8. At the end of the day, we were happy to repose on the grass.

 Find and circle the words with the roots pos, pel, or pul in the puzzle. Some of the words go across, and some go down. Use the word bank to help you.

```
P   X   R   D   I   S   P   E   L   Z
O   R   S   I   Q   W   P   T   S   C
S   V   O   S   Y   H   G   N   D   O
I   U   A   P   X   P   V   C   E   M
T   Q   I   O   O   O   U   X   P   P
I   C   R   S   T   S   Q   L   O   O
V   E   O   E   R   T   E   X   S   S
E   Y   W   M   L   U   W   M   I   E
F   J   G   H   P   R   L   W   T   V
S   Q   Z   R   K   E   L   N   S   Q
J   T   R   E   P   E   L   X   Z   R
```

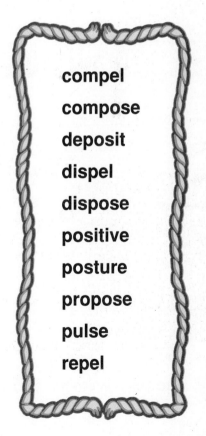

compel

compose

deposit

dispel

dispose

positive

posture

propose

pulse

repel

Fill in the blanks with the word from the word bank that fits the definition. Then write the circled letters on the last line to answer the riddle.

subject	adjectives	portfolio	important
projector	reporter	transported	

1. machine to show movies ____ ____ ____ ____ ____ ____ ____ ____
2. describing words ____ ____ ____ ____ ____ ____ ____ ____
3. having great value ____ ____ ____ ____ ____ ____ ____ ____
4. person who gathers news ____ ____ ____ ____ ____ ____ ____
5. a case for carrying papers ____ ____ ____ ____ ____ ____ ____
6. carried ____ ____ ____ ____ ____ ____ ____ ____ ____
7. topic ____ ____ ____ ____ ____ ____

Riddle

Why did the baby snakes cry? They lost their _____!

Write the word from the word bank that correctly completes the sentence.

8. The _____ of Sasha's science report was the migration of birds.

9. She used colorful_____ to describe the birds.

10. A_____ of famous bird prints was part of Sasha's report.

11. With a movie_____ , Sasha showed films of migrating birds.

12. Like an experienced news_____ , she used a world map to explain bird migratory routes.

13. Sasha explained that bird migration is automatic, almost as if something _____ them south for the winter.

14. Birds use different methods to find their way, including using_____ land forms as markers.

Name _____

Choose the word from the word bank that completes each sentence. Write the word on the line.

HINT

Knowing the meaning of a word root helps you figure out the meaning of a new word. **Aud** means *hear*. **Dict** means *tell* or *say*.

audible = that which can be heard

pre**dict** = to tell what one thinks will happen in the future

1. Kim was class _____ at her graduation.

2. Her teachers _____ she would soon find a job.

3. Kim found a job typing and taking _____ .

4. She worked for a producer of _____ materials, which can be both watched and listened to.

5. When typing, she used a special device to listen to letters that her boss _____ .

6. Kim said that her boss mumbled a lot and had poor _____ .

7. Sometimes his words were barely _____ .

8. When unsure of words, she found a _____ very helpful to check the meanings and spellings.

dictionary	audible
valedictorian	dictation
dictated	diction
predicted	audiovisual

Circle the word that correctly completes each sentence and write it on the line.

9. A ruler who has power over everybody in a country is a _____ .

   valedictorian   dictator   diction

10. A group of people gathered to hear and see something is an _____ .

   audience   audible   audiovisual

11. To say something that is opposite of what someone else has said is to _____ .

   dictation   predict   contradict

Read each word in the list. Underline the prefix and circle the root in each word.

HINT

describe	reduced	introduce
subscribe	deduce	educate
conscript	conduct	produce
education	subscriptions	deduct

Use a word from the words above to complete each sentence. The roots and prefixes will help you find the correct word.

Roots and prefixes can be combined in different ways to create many words. Knowing the meaning of both roots and prefixes can add many words to your vocabulary.

Root: Duct, duc, or **duce** usually means *lead*.

Scribe or **script** usually mean *write* or *something written*.

con**duct** = to lead or guide

in**scribe** = to write, print, carve, or engrave

Prefix: Intro usually means *in* or *into*. **E** usually means *from* or *away*. **Re** usually means *back* or *again*.

introduce = to add or put in

eject = to force out or from

recur = to happen or come again

1. Rick decided to make money by selling magazine

_____ .

2. Rick learned to _____ business in a very professional way.

3. He would knock on doors, _____ himself by giving his name, and ask for orders.

4. Then he would _____ the various magazines on his list in great detail.

5. To promote sales, he offered to _____ the cost of the first issue from the total bill.

6. He found that even though this _____ his initial profits, it increased his total sales.

7. The experience added greatly to his math _____ .

Name _____

Read the sentences and underline the words that contain the roots spec, spect, mit, or miss.

> **HINT**
> Knowing the meaning of a word root helps you figure out the meaning of a new word. **Spec** or **spect** can mean *see, look,* or *examine.* **Mit** or **miss** can mean *send* or *let go.*
>
> in**spect**ed = to look at carefully
>
> dis**miss** = to send away

1. I have to admit it, I love a good mystery novel or movie.

2. I always feel like a spectator at the scene of a crime!

3. My favorite detective is the great Sherlock Holmes, who inspected the smallest details at a crime site.

4. His acute sense of observation enabled him to solve mysteries by deductive speculation.

5. He never dismissed a single shred of evidence as unimportant.

6. Holmes' often permitted his assistant, Dr. Watson, to examine the evidence as well.

7. But Holmes rarely respected anyone's opinions other than his own.

8. Sherlock Holmes amazes me—and the prospect of reading another story about him fills me with . . . well, you read one, you'll see what I mean.

Write the number of each word beside its meaning.

9. admit   _____ to think of as probably guilty

10. dismiss   _____ to acknowledge or confess

11. inspect   _____ a future possibility one is looking for

12. intermission _____ a period between acts in a play

13. permit   _____ to let or allow someone to do something

14. prospect   _____ to send from one's mind

15. respect   _____ to think of someone with admiration

16. spectator   _____ a person who watches or looks at something

17. speculate   _____ to examine or look at carefully

18. suspect   _____ to think about or consider something

Read the words in the box. Underline the root fac, fect, fic, or feit in each word.

factory	counterfeit
defective	effect
fiction	fictitious
perfect	benefactor
facsimile	manufacture

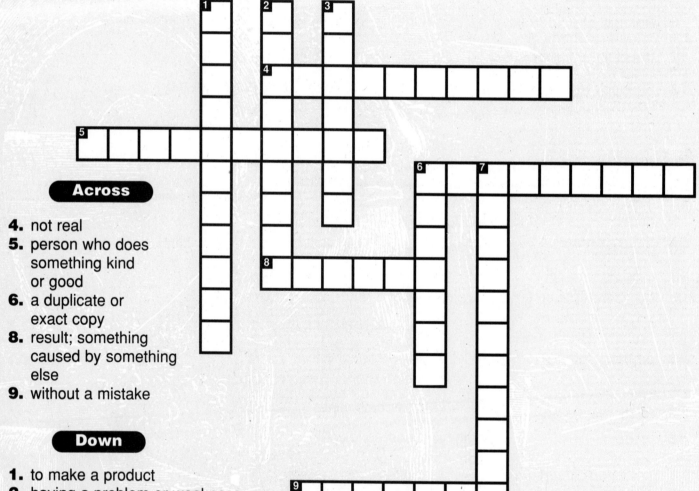 **Use the words in the word bank to work the crossword puzzle.**

Across

4. not real
5. person who does something kind or good
6. a duplicate or exact copy
8. result; something caused by something else
9. without a mistake

Down

1. to make a product
2. having a problem or weakness
3. a place where things can be made
6. piece of writing about something made-up
7. something fake made to fool or cheat people

Read each sentence and underline each compound word. Be sure the words you underline are made up of two words that can stand on their own.

DEFINITION
A **compound word** is made up of two or more smaller words. Each small word can stand alone and still have meaning.

cup + cake = cupcake

dog + house = doghouse

1. Captain Orr spun the dials on the dashboard of the spaceship.

2. She pointed the ship's nose toward the sunrise.

3. The countdown and the blastoff went smoothly.

4. The launch, canceled twice by bad weather, had been overdue.

5. Now came the payoff for the long training of the astronauts.

6. Word of the successful launch was being broadcast nationwide.

7. Dugan watched Captain Orr chew calmly on a toothpick.

8. It was his first spaceflight, and he felt like a boy on his birthday.

9. Someday he would tell his grandchildren of this great adventure.

Find the correct compound word from those you underlined above to match each definition below. Write the word on the line.

10. the instrument panel on a vehicle

_____

11. a vehicle used for travel in outer space

_____

12. beginning of day

_____

13. the launching of a rocket

_____

14. a reward for hard work

_____

15. a radio or television program

_____

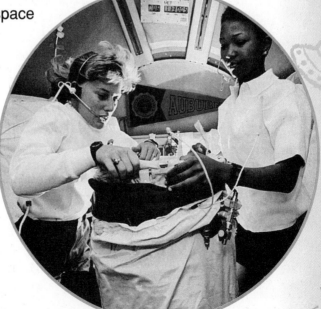

Make compound words by drawing a line from a word in the first column to the word it goes with in the second column. Then write each compound word under the correct heading

1

rain	melon
grape	fly
earth	fruit
blue	bird
water	worm
horse	coat

2

cup	
cat	
over	
neck	
ear	
oat	

3

cake	pan	fish
coat	pea	watch
meal	wrist	neck
ring	star	cakes
fish	turtle	nut
tie	lady	bug

Kinds of Food

1. _____
2. _____
3. _____
4. _____
5. _____
6. _____

Things to Wear

1. _____
2. _____
3. _____
4. _____
5. _____
6. _____

Kinds of Animals

1. _____
2. _____
3. _____
4. _____
5. _____
6. _____

Compound words

Name _____

Read each sentence. Then fill in the circle beside the word that correctly completes the sentence.

How does Tom celebrate his special day? Read the story to find out.

Critical Thinking

DEFINITION

This mark (') is called an apostrophe. An **'s** can be added to a word to show ownership or possession.

Ella**'s** book = a book belonging to Ella

---

1. On Saturday night, Tom threw back the _____ on his bed.

○ covers
○ cover's

---

2. His _____ noisy growling confirmed his hunger.

○ stomach
○ stomach's

---

3. The _____ creaked as he crept down for a late-night snack.

○ stairs
○ stair's

---

4. He heard his _____ voice in the living room.

○ mothers
○ mother's

---

5. Sunday was the _____ tenth birthday.

○ boys
○ boy's

---

6. His _____ were planning a surprise party.

○ parents
○ parent's

---

7. On Sunday he obeyed his _____ call to come downstairs.

○ sisters
○ sister's

---

8. Twenty _____ yelled "Happy Birthday!"

○ voices
○ voice's

---

9. A _____ wheel peeked through the huge package.

○ bikes
○ bike's

---

10. _____ surprise was real, but it had nothing to do with the party.

○ Toms
○ Tom's

Read each sentence below. Write the correct possessive form of the word you see below the line. Look back at the rules if you need to.

1. _____ greatest wish was to
   _{Maria}
   explore caves.

2. There are many caves to explore in her
   _____ hills.
   _{community}

3. She tried to get her _____
   _{parents}
   permission to go exploring.

4. "It isn't a safe _____
   _{children}
   hobby," her mother said.

5. Her Dad belongs to a _____
   _{men}
   group for spelunkers, or cave explorers.

6. She finally got her _____
   _{father}
   promise to take her exploring.

7. They invited Ron, _____ friend, to
   _{Maria}
   go with them.

8. Ron's father belongs to the cave
   _____ group, too.
   _{explorers}

9. On the _____ first cave visit,
   _{friends}
   they heard a strange noise.

10. It was the sound of hundreds of
    _____ wings.
    _{bats}

11. Maria ran back to the _____ mouth.
    _{cave}

12. Neither Maria nor Ron have asked to explore a
    _____ cave since!
    _{bat}

Do you think Maria and Ron will want to explore a cave again? Why or why not?

Critical Thinking

Name _____

On the first line, write the contraction from the word bank that stands for each pair of words. Then, on the second line, write the letter or letters that have been left out.

DEFINITION

A **contraction** is a short way of writing two words. The two words are written together with one or more letters left out. An apostrophe stands for the missing letters.

it is = **it's** (The letter **i** has been left out.)

I will = **I'll** (The letters **wi** have been left out.)

We are = **we're** (The letter **a** has been left out.)

---

wouldn't	you're	they'll
didn't	we're	I'm
it's	we'll	I've

1. we are   _____   ___

2. did not   _____   ___

3. I am   _____   ___

4. would not   _____   ___

5. they will   _____   ___

6. you are   _____   ___

7. it is   _____   ___

8. I have   _____   ___

9. we will   _____   ___

can't	she'll	you've	that's
let's	don't	he's	isn't

10. she will   _____   ___

11. you have   _____   ___

12. is not   _____   ___

13. let us   _____   ___

14. he is   _____   ___

15. can not   _____   ___

16. that is   _____   ___

17. do not   _____   ___

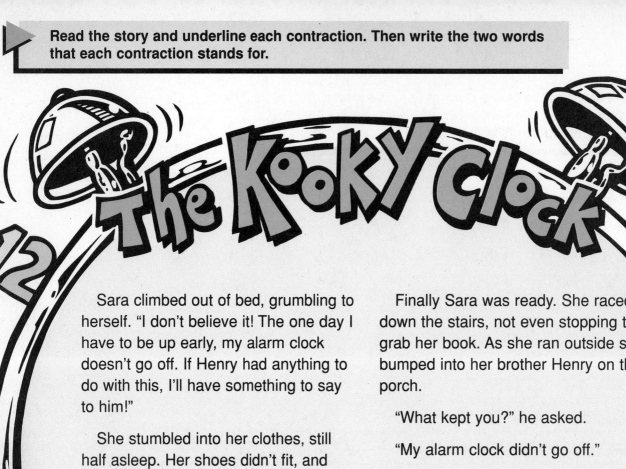

The Kooky Clock

Sara climbed out of bed, grumbling to herself. "I don't believe it! The one day I have to be up early, my alarm clock doesn't go off. If Henry had anything to do with this, I'll have something to say to him!"

She stumbled into her clothes, still half asleep. Her shoes didn't fit, and she realized she hadn't put them on the right feet. "Let's get this together," she muttered. "I'm not going to miss the last day of the spelling contest. Nancy's going to be at school early. I know she'll be there before anybody else so she can get some extra study time."

Finally Sara was ready. She raced down the stairs, not even stopping to grab her book. As she ran outside she bumped into her brother Henry on the porch.

"What kept you?" he asked.

"My alarm clock didn't go off."

"I hope it wasn't my fault. I set it last night so it would go off early," Henry explained. "At least that's what I thought I did."

"Well, you've got a lot to learn about clocks," said Sara. "Come on, or we'll both be late. I can't miss the contest!"

1. _____

2. _____

3. _____

4. _____

5. _____

6. _____

7. _____

8. _____

9. _____

10. _____

11. _____

12. _____

13. _____

14. _____

15. _____

Name _____

Say each word. On the first line, write the number of syllables it has. Then write the word and divide it into syllables, using vertical lines.

HINT
A word has as many syllables as it has vowel sounds. A prefix is a syllable in itself if it contains a vowel sound. Divide the word between the prefix and the base word. Remember that some prefixes have more than one syllable.

re/turn   an/ti/dote

1. dispose _____ _____

2. subject _____ _____

3. predict _____ _____

4. audible _____ _____

5. introduce _____ _____

6. reduce _____ _____

7. permit _____ _____

8. spectator _____ _____

9. defect _____ _____

10. posture _____ _____

11. subdivide _____ _____

12. biennial _____ _____

13. transport _____ _____

14. dictation _____ _____

15. subscribe _____ _____

16. mission _____ _____

17. counterfeit _____ _____

18. perfect _____ _____

19. deceive _____ _____

20. expect _____ _____

21. conduct _____ _____

22. reporter _____ _____

23. postscript _____ _____

24. submerge _____ _____

Read each sentence, find the missing word, and write it on the line.

25. Mom said I could _____ to the magazine for the summer.

subscribe
subject

26. A _____ from a magazine interviewed the girl who saved the drowning child.

reporter
spectator

Write each compound word and divide it into two words, using vertical lines. If necessary, divide the smaller words into syllables.

1. seashells _____

2. strawberry _____

3. everyone _____

4. skyscraper _____

5. seashore _____

6. footprints _____

7. buttonhole _____

8. overcoat _____

9. clothespin _____

10. classmate _____

11. anthill _____

12. workbook _____

13. wristwatch _____

14. sailboat _____

15. mailbox _____

16. newspaper _____

17. fingerprint _____

18. watermelon _____

Write the word from above that completes each sentence.

19. This year the class outing was held at the _____ .

20. One _____ had never seen the ocean before.

21. Sarah saw a sand dune and thought it looked like a giant _____ .

22. Carl enjoyed watching a _____ drift in the water.

23. Louis searched for pretty _____ in the sand.

24. We saw a dog's _____ on the beach.

25. Our teacher looked at her _____ and said it was time to go.

26. At the end of the day, _____ went home tired but happy.

Name _____

 Reading Abby took a camping vacation with her family to a National Park in the western United States. Read the following entry from her travel diary. Then answer the question at the end of the story.

Dear Diary,   August 27

Today was the most exciting day of my life! This afternoon my grandfather proposed we take a horseback ride. Perhaps I'd better describe how I feel about horses. It's not that I'm repelled by them, but I am terrified to use them as transportation.

The rest of the family doesn't feel the same way. My younger brother has gone on many trail rides. My dad's favorite activity at summer camp was riding. My mom's love for horses started when she was little. So when the trail guide said, "I've inspected everyone's saddles. It's time to introduce yourself to your horse," my family was thrilled. I felt sick.

"Hello, Juniper," I whispered to my horse. "I'm Abby, and I hope this summer heat makes you feel sleepy." Just then, Juniper let out a whinny and bucked in the air, not once, but twice! "Hold onto the reins and clasp your legs around the horse's body!" yelled the guide. When Juniper took off, lots of people yelled at him to stop, but he didn't listen.

The horse's pace slowed down when the trail got rocky, and soon the guide galloped alongside and grabbed the reins. "You know what," she said, "you're a born rider!"

Why do you think Abby was so excited about her day? Give reasons for your answers.

_____

_____

_____

_____

_____

_____

 **Writing**

Suppose you were the guide on Abby's trail ride. Write a letter to your parents, describing what happened on the trail ride. Use at least five words from the word bank. Below are some questions to help you.

audience	didn't	horses'
cowgirl	important	parents'
I'm	permitted	positive
perfect	predicted	she'd
		sunset

What happened?

Who was involved?

What contributed to the problem?

How did you solve it?

Helpful Hints

Review roots, compounds, possessives, contractions: Writing

Name _____

Fill in the circle beside the answer that best completes each sentence.

1. To place something for safekeeping is to ____ it.
   - ○ predict
   - ○ deposit
   - ○ perfect

2. A book that gives the correct spelling of words is a ____ .
   - ○ dictionary
   - ○ dictaphone
   - ○ conductor

3. To carry something from one place to another is to ____ it.
   - ○ dismiss
   - ○ transport
   - ○ reduce

4. A building where goods are made is a ____ .
   - ○ spectator
   - ○ portfolio
   - ○ factory

5. To write or tell about something in detail is to ____ it.
   - ○ eject
   - ○ contradict
   - ○ describe

6. To look at something carefully is to ____ it.
   - ○ inspect
   - ○ reject
   - ○ deduct

Fill in the circle beside the answer that best describes the underlined word.

7. Lisa is excited about her visit to her <u>grandparents'</u> farm.
   - ○ contraction
   - ○ possessive

8. <u>She's</u> been looking forward to visiting the farm for a long time.
   - ○ contraction
   - ○ possessive

9. <u>There's</u> always something happening on the farm.
   - ○ contraction
   - ○ possessive

10. Last year, someone accidentally left open the <u>horses'</u> pen.
    - ○ contraction
    - ○ possessive

11. It was nearly dark by the time <u>they'd</u> rounded up all the horses.
    - ○ contraction
    - ○ possessive

12. That night, horses–not sheep–jumped fences in <u>Lisa's</u> dreams.
    - ○ contraction
    - ○ possessive

Read the words in the word bank. Then read the paragraphs. Write the correct word from the word bank on the line to complete each sentence. Then answer the questions.

educated	important	seashore	misuse
grandparents'	weekend	spectators	lawmakers
I'll	sailboats	subject	environmental

Honoring Rachel Carson

Last summer, a special anniversary was celebrated at the Rachel Carson Salt Pond Preserve, next to the _____ near the town of Round Pond, Maine. That weekend, people came on foot, on bicycles, in canoes and kayaks, and even in _____ , to celebrate the life and work of Rachel Carson. She was a prominent scientist and writer who _____ the public about protecting the environment. The _____ of her most famous book, *Silent Spring,* was the _____ of pesticides. This _____ book helped convince _____ to pass legislation requiring _____ protection measures.

Because my _____ cottage is near the salt pond, my friend Rebecca and I were _____ for all the activities. We learned a lot about an important woman. When she left, Rebecca said, "_____ remember this _____ forever!"

1. Why did people come to this specific salt pond in Maine?

_____

_____

2. What effect did Rachel Carson's writings have on the environment?

_____

_____

Which conveniences could you live without? Why? What would you do instead?

Critical Thinking

Have you considered what your life would be like without the modern conveniences, or inventions, we use every day? Look at the picture carefully. Circle the conveniences you find.

Dear Family,

In the next few weeks, your child will be learning about adding suffixes to words and how a suffix can change the meaning and the structure of a word. Suffixes are word parts that come at the end of base words. Some of the suffixes we'll be studying include **or** as in invent**or**, **ful** as in thought**ful**, **ness** as in happi**ness**, **est** as in saf**est**, and **able** as in wash**able**.

At-Home Activities

▶ Talk with your child about some of the conveniences in your home and the tasks they help you do. How would the family do the same tasks without those inventions?

▶ With your child, think of a new invention that would help make your life easier. Then draw up a plan of what your invention looks like. If you can, construct a model out of materials on hand, such as cardboard, construction paper, glue, and staples.

▶ Encourage your child to interview an older relative, friend, or neighbor about the conveniences available during that person's childhood. Invite your child to ask questions such as these: How was your childhood different from mine?; What did you do for fun?

Book Corner

You and your child might enjoy reading these books together. Look for them in your local library.

Winter Camp
by Kirkpatrick Hill

Two orphans learn the customs and traditions of their Athabascan roots when they spend the winter with their elderly neighbor.

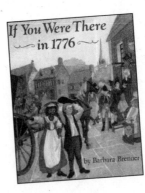

If You Were There in 1776
by Barbara Brenner

Learn about the rigors and joys of everyday life during the time of the American Revolution.

Sincerely,

Name _____

Add **er, or,** or **ist** to each word to make a noun. If a word ends with **e** or **y**, remember to drop the **e** or **y** before adding the suffix.

RULES

The suffixes **er** and **or** can change a verb into a noun that means *someone who does something* or a *thing that can do something*. The suffix **ist** changes a noun that means *a thing* into a noun that means *someone who does something.*

lead**er** = someone who leads

collect**or** = someone who collects

novel**ist** = someone who writes novels

1. interpret _____

2. teach _____

3. real _____

4. train _____

5. counsel _____

6. archaeology _____

7. novel _____

8. bake _____

9. project _____

10. visit _____

11. paint _____

12. act _____

Write one of the words you made above to complete each sentence.

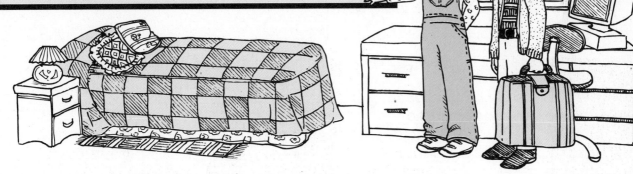

13. Nancy fixed up the guest room for a special _____.

14. Nancy's teacher and school _____ had assigned her an exchange student.

15. Nancy thought they would need an _____ to communicate.

16. Her guest speaks English as well as Nancy's English _____.

17. Her guest wants to be an _____ who studies old cities.

18. Nancy says she'd like to be a best-selling _____.

Underline the word in each sentence with the suffix ward, en, or ize. Then write a short definition of the word on the line.

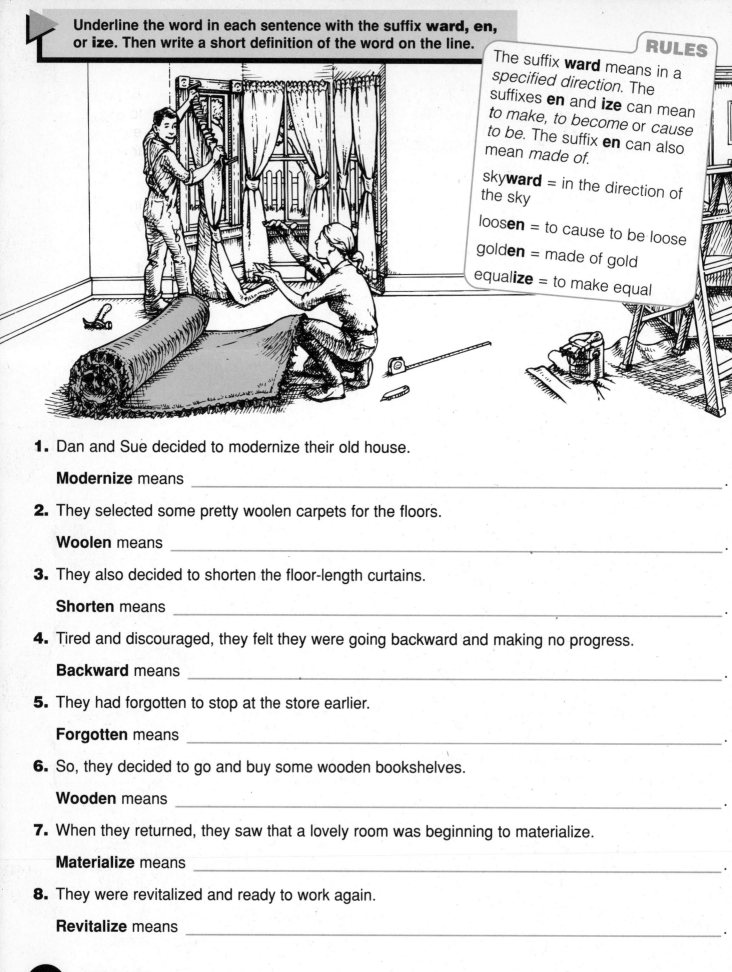

1. Dan and Sue decided to modernize their old house.

Modernize means _____.

2. They selected some pretty woolen carpets for the floors.

Woolen means _____.

3. They also decided to shorten the floor-length curtains.

Shorten means _____.

4. Tired and discouraged, they felt they were going backward and making no progress.

Backward means _____.

5. They had forgotten to stop at the store earlier.

Forgotten means _____.

6. So, they decided to go and buy some wooden bookshelves.

Wooden means _____.

7. When they returned, they saw that a lovely room was beginning to materialize.

Materialize means _____.

8. They were revitalized and ready to work again.

Revitalize means _____.

Name _____

▶ **Read each sentence and the two words below the line. Choose the word that best completes the sentence and write it on the line.**

RULE

The suffixes **er** and **est** are added to adjectives to make them show comparison

Today is **hot.**

Today is **hotter** than yesterday. (Two days are compared.)

Today is the **hottest** day of the year. (More than two days are compared.)

1. Troy, Niles, and Lowell are three

   _____ places to live.
   (nice, nicest)

2. Troy is a _____ town than Lowell.
   (bigger, biggest)

3. Niles is the _____ town of the three.
   (bigger, biggest)

4. Of the three towns, Jay thinks Troy has the _____ people.
   (friendlier, friendliest)

5. Compared with Niles, Jay thinks Lowell has a _____ downtown.
   (prettier, prettiest)

6. The flowers downtown are the _____ he has ever seen.
   (prettier, prettiest)

7. All three towns have _____ high school football teams.
   (great, greatest)

8. This year, Niles was ranked _____ than Lowell.
   (higher, highest)

9. But, Niles was ranked _____ than Troy.
   (lower, lowest)

10. Of the three towns, Troy had the _____
    football team.   (better, best)

11. Jay would be _____ living in any one of the towns.
    (happy, happiest)

How does your town compare to Troy, Niles, or Lowell?

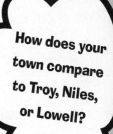

Critical Thinking

weak   weaker   weakest

1. The radio signals grew _____ as the evening storm wore on.

They were _____ when the storm began. But they became the

_____ during the heavy thunder and lightning.

large   larger   largest

2. The sales clerk showed me some _____ sweats. They were

_____ than the ones I have at home. In fact they were the

_____ sweats I'd ever seen!

hungry   hungrier   hungriest

3. Tad is the _____ boy I have ever known. He is usually

_____ at dinner than he is at lunch. But then, he is

_____ most of the time.

dirty   dirtier   dirtiest

4. Last Saturday we washed our _____ car. The inside windows

were the _____ parts on the whole car. The hubcaps were

even _____ than they were the last time we washed them.

early   earlier   earliest

5. Ana gets up the _____ of anyone in our class.

Alex thinks he gets up _____ , but even I get up

_____ than he does!

Name

> **Read each sentence. Write a definition for the underlined word on the line below the sentence.**

> **RULES**
>
> The suffix **eer** usually means *someone who*. The suffixes **ee, ent,** and **ant** can also mean *someone who*. These suffixes can also mean *that which*.
>
> puppet**eer** = someone who works puppets
>
> pay**ee** = someone who is paid
>
> repell**ent** = that which repels
>
> serv**ant** = someone who serves

1. The current occupants are moving out of the apartment.

   Occupant means _____ .

2. First they hired an auctioneer to sell some of their belongings.

   Auctioneer means _____ .

3. Then they hired several assistants to help them move their other things.

   Assistant means _____ .

4. The assistants are employees of the local moving company.

   Employee means _____ .

5. Even some of the dependents of the moving company employees came to help.

   Dependent means _____ .

6. The occupants voted in today's election by absentee ballot.

   Absentee means _____ .

7. They wanted to be sure to get to vote for the new president.

   President means _____ .

8. They were also anxious to elect a good school superintendent.

   Superintendent means _____ .

9. There will be a new city engineer this year, too.

   Engineer means _____ .

10. However, that person will be an appointee, not an elected official.

    Appointee means _____ .

Lesson 54
Suffixes -ee, -eer, -ent, -ant

119

© MCP All rights reserved. Copying strictly prohibited.

1. Ben is an _____ and will be on a business trip on election day.

puppeteer
engineer

2. Since he will be away, he is voting by _____ ballot.

absentee
payee

3. One of the issues on the ballot is especially _____ to Ben.

important
accountant

4. It will affect where his _____ go to school.

repellents
dependents

5. One _____ to the school board has suggested some school boundary changes.

appointee
payee

6. Ben is a _____ of one of the areas that would be affected.

precedent
resident

7. Therefore, he is an _____ of those who are proposing the change.

assistant
opponent

8. Another _____ who works with Ben is also opposed to the boundary changes.

employee
contestant

9. Some people have been very _____ in campaigning about the boundary issue.

persistent
absorbent

10. Unfortunately, many others are _____ of the proposed changes.

dependent
ignorant

Critical Thinking

Why is it important for all citizens to vote?

Name

Choose one word from the word bank to complete each of the following sentences. Write the word on the line.

RULES

When added to a word to make an adjective, the suffix **ful** means *full of* or *having a tendency to.* When added to a word to make a noun, **ful** means *a certain amount.* The suffix **ness** means *the quality or condition of being.*

cheer**ful** = an adjective that means full of cheer

play**ful** = having a tendency to play

new**ness** = the condition of being new

quietness	darkness	plentiful
spoonful	harmful	peaceful
successful	armful	mouthfuls
coolness	sleepiness	useful

1. Pat and Lynn chose a very relaxing and _____ campsite.

2. The _____ was a pleasant relief from the noise of the city.

3. Lynn gathered an _____ of logs for the campfire.

4. Pat was _____ in building a roaring fire.

5. They were surprised at the _____ of the air after the sun went down.

6. The fire not only kept them warm but made enough light so they could easily see in the _____.

7. It also helped keep away _____ animals.

8. Lynn cooked some stew and scooped a large _____ onto Pat's plate.

9. After several _____, Pat said, "That's delicious!"

10. The stew was _____, so Pat had a second helping.

11. The firelight was _____ as they washed their dishes.

12. They sat and talked until _____ caused them to settle down for the night.

Do you think Pat and Lynn had been camping before? How do you know?

Critical Thinking

Read each sentence and the words below it. Fill in the circle beside the word that best completes the sentence.

1. Lydia asked her mother to ___ plan her wedding.
   ○ help   ○ helped   ○ helpful

2. Lydia wanted the most ___ wedding she could afford.
   ○ beauty   ○ beautify   ○ beautiful

3. She wanted all her friends to share in her ___.
   ○ happiness   ○ happier   ○ happy

4. Much ___ planning was necessary.
   ○ caring   ○ careful   ○ carefully

5. Her fiancé, Steve, was very ___ with the wedding plans.
   ○ help   ○ helpful   ○ helper

6. He made some ___ suggestions for the wedding ceremony.
   ○ use   ○ user   ○ useful

7. Lydia's mother was impressed by Steve's ___.
   ○ thoughtful   ○ thoughtfulness ○ thoughtless

8. She began to see what a ___ person Steve was.
   ○ kind   ○ kinder   ○ kindness

9. She was ___ her daughter was marrying such a fine man.
   ○ glad   ○ gladly   ○ gladness

10. All of the planning had a ___ result.
    ○ success   ○ successful   ○ succession

11. Everyone who came to the wedding had a ___ time.
    ○ delight   ○ delighted   ○ delightful

12. Steven and Lydia's ___ towards each other was obvious.
    ○ tenderly   ○ tenderness   ○ tender

13. Their wedding was the start of a ___ life together.
    ○ wonderful   ○ wondered   ○ wondering

Why is thoughtfulness important?

Critical Thinking

Lesson 55
Suffixes -ful, -ness

Name _____

▶ **Read the following paragraph. Circle each word that has the suffix hood, ship, or ment.**

Our neighborhood track team won the championship this fall. There was a lot of excitement over this accomplishment. The likelihood of the township buying trophies for the members of the team was high. Matt Evans' leadership is one factor in the team's improvement this season. There is no argument about that! He has encouraged both trust and friendship among team members. We are still in amazement at the change in our team's attitude!

> **RULES**
>
> The suffixes **hood, ship,** and **ment** usually mean *the state or condition of being.*
>
> child**hood** = the state or condition of being a child
>
> leader**ship** = the state or condition of being a leader
>
> retire**ment** = state or condition of being retired

▶ **Now write the correct circled word on the line next to its definition.**

1. something done well _____

2. place where people live _____

   or _____

3. probability _____

4. something that has gotten better _____

5. quarrel _____

6. state of being friends _____

7. first place position _____

8. great thrill _____

9. guidance, direction _____

10. great surprise, astonishment _____

> **Add the suffix hood, ship, or ment** to each word below to form a new word. Write the new word on the line.

1. child _____

2. likely _____

3. relation _____

4. equip _____

5. friend _____

6. enjoy _____

7. author _____

8. retire _____

9. neighbor _____

10. excite _____

> **Write one of the words you made above** to complete each of the following sentences. Use each word only once.

11. Since Grandpa's _____ from work, he and Juan do many things together.

12. Juan and Grandpa have always had a good _____ .

13. Grandpa enjoyed telling Juan stories of his early _____ days.

14. In those days, Grandpa lived on a farm, not in a close-knit _____ .

15. He told Juan how he learned to use heavy farm _____ as a child.

16. Grandpa told Juan about the _____ of harvesting crops on the farm.

17. Juan and Grandpa share the _____ of a story they wrote.

18. It is about the _____ between a young boy and his grandfather.

19. There is not much _____ of the story ever being published.

20. What is important is the _____ they got from writing it!

Name _____

RULE

The suffixes **able** and **ible** usually mean *able to be* or *full of*.

wash**able** = able to be washed

sens**ible** = full of sense

1. When clothing can be cleaned in water,

it is called _____ .

washable   reversible

2. Something that can be made smaller is

_____ .

reducible   defensible

3. An activity that makes lots of money is _____ .

collapsible   profitable

4. Something that can be damaged if it is dropped is _____ .

breakable   adorable

5. A jacket that can be worn with either side out is _____ .

reversible   reducible

6. Food that is not spoiled is _____ .

eatable   excitable

7. Something that can be changed or moved to make it fit is _____ .

adjustable   dependable

8. Something that can spoil easily is _____ .

perishable   reducible

9. Something that can be defended is _____ .

dependable   defensible

10. Someone who can be trusted or depended upon is _____ .

reducible   responsible

11. An object that can be folded together and put in a smaller package is

_____ .

reversible   collapsible

12. A book is something that is _____ .

eatable   readable

13. When someone is intelligent, we say that he or she is _____ .

knowledgeable   fashionable

Read the words in the word bank. Underline the suffix able or ible in each word.

memorable	comfortable	accessible	movable
collapsible	adjustable	dependable	responsible
usable	sensible	enjoyable	reducible

 Use the base words to complete the crossword puzzle.

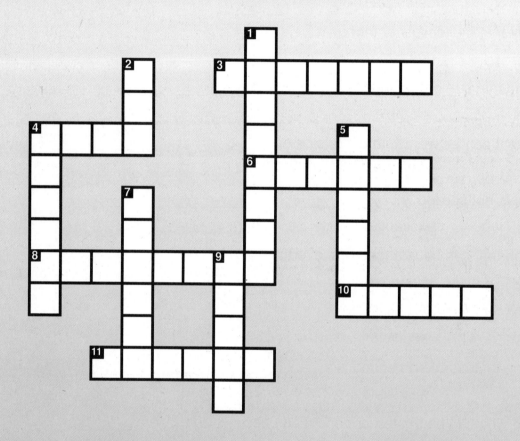

Across

3. to soothe someone who is sad
4. to change position
6. a way to get into or reach some place
8. an answer
10. to do something that makes you happy
11. to move to a different position

Down

1. to fall down; to fold together
2. to put into service for a particular purpose
4. something that is remembered
5. to make smaller
7. to trust; to be certain about
9. good judgment

Suffixes -able, -ible

Name

RULES

The suffixes **ion, ation,** and **ition** usually mean *the act of or the condition of being.*

exhaus**tion** = the condition of being exhausted

invit**ation** = the act of inviting

add**ition** = the act of adding

1. The lives of ordinary Americans have been the subjects of many different

   forms of artistic _____ .
   (expressed, expression)

2. Photographer Dorothea Lange, for example, depicted the plight of migrant workers

   during the Depression (1929–1938) in her photographic _____ .
   (compositions, composed)

3. As she traveled throughout the country during this time, she was _____
   (fascination, fascinated)

   by the people she met.

4. The _____ for many of her photographs was the courage
   (inspiration, inspired)

   she saw in the lives of many struggling Americans.

5. Walker Evans was another photographer whose work _____
   (illustrations, illustrated)

   the widespread poverty of the Depression years.

6. In _____ to their stark lines, his photographs showed a
   (addition, add)

   remarkable understanding of his subjects.

7. The _____ of the lives of ordinary Americans has also
   (depicted, depiction)

   been the focus of many American painters.

8. If you ever have the chance to see a _____ of the paintings
   (presented, presentation)

   of Andrew Wyeth, be sure to go!

9. A _____ of his work illustrates his understanding of the
   (selected, selection)

   beauty and grace of nature.

Add the suffix **ion**, **ation**, or **ition** to each word below to form a new word. Write the new word on the line.

RULE

When a word ends with **e**, drop the **e** before adding **ion**, **ation**, or **ition**.

elate + **ion** = elat**ion**

realize + **ation** = realiz**ation**

compose = **ition** = compos**ition**

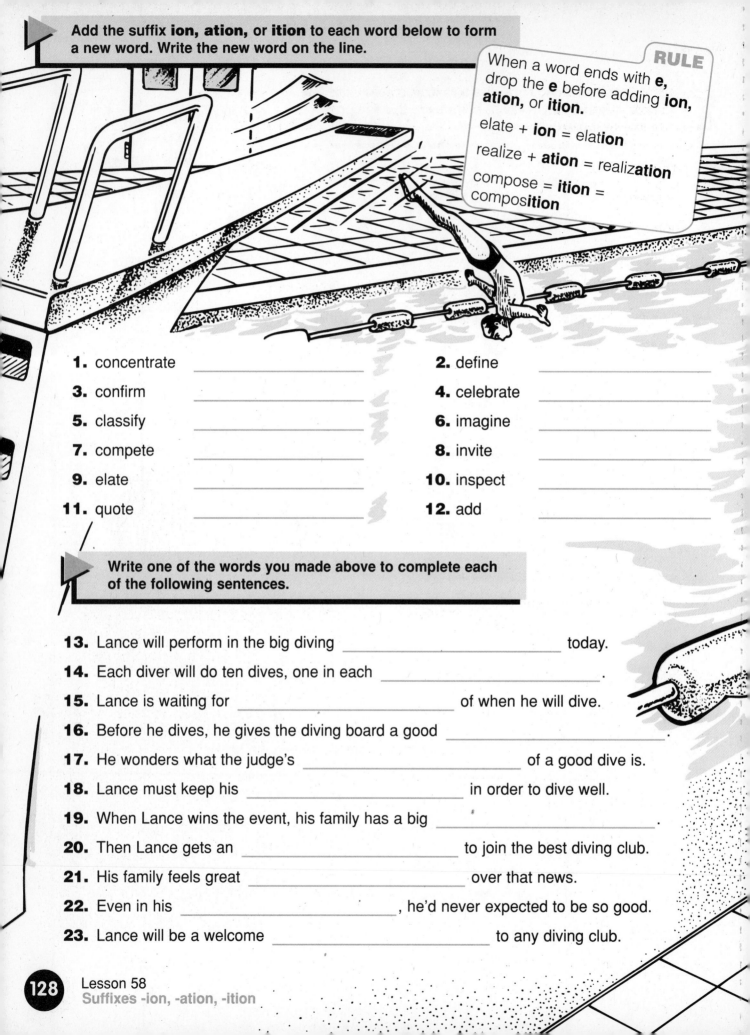

1. concentrate _____
2. define _____
3. confirm _____
4. celebrate _____
5. classify _____
6. imagine _____
7. compete _____
8. invite _____
9. elate _____
10. inspect _____
11. quote _____
12. add _____

Write one of the words you made above to complete each of the following sentences.

13. Lance will perform in the big diving _____ today.

14. Each diver will do ten dives, one in each _____.

15. Lance is waiting for _____ of when he will dive.

16. Before he dives, he gives the diving board a good _____.

17. He wonders what the judge's _____ of a good dive is.

18. Lance must keep his _____ in order to dive well.

19. When Lance wins the event, his family has a big _____.

20. Then Lance gets an _____ to join the best diving club.

21. His family feels great _____ over that news.

22. Even in his _____, he'd never expected to be so good.

23. Lance will be a welcome _____ to any diving club.

Name _____

Write the base word and the suffix that were combined to make each of the following words.

1. publicity = _____ + _____

2. confidence = _____ + _____

3. impressive = _____ + _____

4. acceptance = _____ + _____

5. active   = _____ + _____

6. sincerity = _____ + _____

7. creative   = _____ + _____

Use the words above in the sentences. Use each word only once.

8. Tara is always busy because she is

   _____ in so many groups.

9. She creates _____

   for the groups so that new members will join.

10. She is a very caring person and shows it by

    her _____ .

11. She always has unique ideas because she is

    so _____ .

12. Other group members have great

    _____ in Tara's skills.

13. Whatever Tara is in charge of always ends up being

    done in a very _____ way.

14. This year, Tara won an award and gave a

    fine _____ speech.

Circle the correct word to complete each analogy. Then write the word.

1. **Dynamite** is to **explosive** as **tape** is to _____.

   adhesive   impressive   selective

2. **Helping** is to **assistance** as **watching** is to _____.

   hindrance   observance   coincidence

3. **Negativity** is to **positivity** as **criminality** is to _____.

   simplicity   complexity   legality

4. **Dance** is to **activity** as **uproar** is to _____.

   disturbance   attendance   guidance

5. **Insecurity** is to **confidence** as **sameness** is to _____.

   residence   conference   difference

6. **Leading** is to **guidance** as **forgiving** is to _____.

   insurance   tolerance   observance

7. **Offense** is to **defense** as **superiority** is to _____.

   inferiority   security   popularity

8. **Unusual** is to **distinctive** as **pretty** is to _____.

   attractive   selective   executive

9. **Advertisement** is to **publicity** as **generator** is to _____.

   mortality   electricity   legality

10. **Hot** is to **cold** as **active** is to _____.

    passive   negative   disruptive

11. **Modesty** is to **arrogance** as **gentleness** is to _____.

    reference   violence   absence

12. **Try** is to **attempt** as **escape** is to _____.

    avoidance   annoyance   resistance

Name _____

Helping Out

Have you ever thought about how you and your classmates can make your community, or even the world, a better place to live? You'd be surprised at how many different kinds of projects you can do once you decide to get involved!

What's the first step? Choose an issue that's important to you and your friends and classmates. Then make a list of possible projects related to the issue. Are you and your classmates interested in the environment? Then you might consider cleaning up litter in your neighborhood or starting a paper recycling project at your school. If you are interested in helping animals, you can help animal shelters find homes for abandoned pets by making posters or writing a letter to the local newspaper. Or, if you prefer working with people, volunteering at a senior citizens home is a great place to start.

Once you have chosen a useful project, find a teacher, counselor, or parent to help you make a plan. Think about your goals. Be persistent, but be realistic! The important thing is to get involved. You'll discover that you *can* make a difference in your neighborhood—and in your world!

What are some issues you care about?

_____

_____

_____

_____

_____

_____

 **Writing**

Choose an issue and think of a project you and your classmates could do. Use the helpful hints and at least five words from the word bank.

What is an issue you care about?

How can you do something about it?

What will your project accomplish?

What is your plan of action?

 **Helpful Hints**

friendship
teacher
responsible
organization
improvement
persistent
ignorant
preparation
neighborhood
important
successful
accomplishment

GLASS

Name _____

UNIT 5 CHECKUP

Read each sentence and the suffixes that follow it. Notice the base word in dark print. Fill in the circle beside the suffix that should be added to the base word.

1. The **novel**_____ wrote a mystery book.
   ○ ist   ○ or   ○ eer

2. The **auction**_____ yelled, "Sold!"
   ○ ent   ○ eer   ○ ist

3. Tony moved **for**_____ two spaces.
   ○ ward   ○ ant   ○ est

4. The seal **train**_____ used fish as a reward.
   ○ eer   ○ er   ○ ist

5. Let's **revital**_____ the neighborhood.
   ○ ize   ○ eer   ○ ist

6. Only one **visit**_____ is allowed in the room.
   ○ ant   ○ or   ○ ee

7. An **account**_____ balanced our checkbook.
   ○ er   ○ or   ○ ant

8. Because Juan was away, he used an **absent**_____ ballot.
   ○ ee   ○ er   ○ ize

9. The forest was quiet and **peace**_____.
   ○ ward   ○ ness   ○ ful

10. The **happi**_____ of the family was easy to see.
    ○ ness   ○ est   ○ ful

11. Our class won the spelling **champion**_____ this year.
    ○ ment   ○ ship   ○ ence

12. My skating showed a lot of **improve**_____ this winter.
    ○ able   ○ tion   ○ ment

13. I am **respons**_____ for my pet frog.
    ○ ible   ○ able   ○ ment

14. That building is the **high**_____ one in the city.
    ○ est   ○ er   ○ ist

15. Our soccer team is **unbeat**_____.
    ○ able   ○ ive   ○ ence

16. Our players run **fast**_____ than our opponents.
    ○ est   ○ er   ○ or

17. The classroom **add**_____ gives us more space.
    ○ hood   ○ ence   ○ ition

18. I love living in this **neighbor**_____.
    ○ ence   ○ ship   ○ hood

19. I like to be **creat**_____ in art class.
    ○ ive   ○ ness   ○ ful

20. I can't tell the **differ**_____ between these two drawings.
    ○ ence   ○ able   ○ ful

Read the words in the word bank. Then read the article. Write the correct word from the word bank on the line to complete each sentence. Then answer the questions.

advertisements	competition	creative	durability
imaginations	impressive	knowledgeable	likelihood
passive	responsible	selection	sincerity

Have you ever considered how many times a day you are bombarded by all types of _____? Advertising is a multi-billion dollar industry. Advertisers try to persuade consumers to buy a particular product or service. Since the _____ among products is fierce, thousands of _____ people use their _____ every day to develop clever ads they hope will capture your attention.

What is the _____ that an intelligent, _____ consumer will be affected by ads? It's very high! But you can be a _____ consumer by researching a product before you buy it. For example, if you plan to buy a pair of athletic shoes, compare a wide _____ of shoes. Look at the features, price, and _____ of the shoes. Ask yourself whether this is the best pair of shoes for the price I can afford, or am I being swayed by a clever ad or the seeming _____ of a celebrity spokesperson?

Remember that no matter how clever or _____ an ad might be, you should make an active decision, not a _____ one about what to buy and when to buy it.

1. What is the purpose of advertising?

_____

_____

2. What are some ways you can be a knowledgeable consumer?

_____

_____

FUN WITH MORE THAN ONE!

When you walk by the lake,
You might see a goose,
Who will probably lead you to geese.
But if you happen upon a moose
Don't look for a number of meese!

More than one moose
Is two or three moose,
But more than one mouse
Is two mice!

So if you live in one house in the city,
And another small house by the lake,
Then you live in two houses,
Not in two hice,
So please, don't make that mistake!

Do you ever get confused when you're talking about more than one of something? Read the poem to help you remember!

If you're unsure of the plural form of a word, how can you find out what it is?

Critical Thinking

Home Letter

Dear Family,

In the next few weeks, your child will be learning about words that have irregular plurals such as child/children and mouse/mice as well as more about suffixes. We'll be learning how the spelling of base words that end in silent e and in y change when a suffix is added, for example, busy/busier and combine/combining.

At-Home Activities

▶ Look at the poem and illustration on the other side of this letter with your child. Then read the poem together.

▶ Find the nine items that appear alone and in a group in the picture and write the singular and plural names for them. It's okay to check a dictionary if you're not sure of the plural forms of the words!

▶ With your child, think of 3 things with irregular plurals. Then compose a verse to add to the poem on the other side of this page.

Book Corner

You and your child might enjoy reading these books together. Look for them in your local library.

Mrs. Cole on an Onion Roll

by Kalli Dakos

Children of all ages will appreciate the humor in this collection of wacky poems about elementary school life.

If I Were in Charge of the World

by Judith Viorst

This series of forty-one humorous poems adds a poetic dimension to everyday life.

Sincerely,

Name _____

▶ **Form new words by combining each base word and suffix. Write the new words on the lines.**

1. rub + ing _____

2. laugh + ing _____

3. jog + ing _____

4. quick + est _____

5. rob + er _____

6. chap + ed _____

7. start + ing _____

8. strut + ed _____

9. hit + er _____

10. fat + est _____

11. plan + ing _____

12. stun + ed _____

13. fast + er _____

14. skid + ed _____

15. grin + ing _____

16. refresh + ed _____

▶ **Read each sentence and circle the correct suffix in parentheses. Write the new word on the line.**

17. I think holidays are the great (er, est) days of the year. _____

18. I clap (est, ed) loudly at the Fourth of July celebration. _____

19. Crowds jam (est, ed) the roads for the Thanksgiving parade. _____

20. Government lead (ers, ing) marched in the parade. _____

21. Plan (ed, ing) the annual Memorial Day picnic was fun. _____

22. Chat (ing, er) with friends is my favorite holiday pastime. _____

Words that double the final consonant to add a suffix

Circle each suffix below that begins with a vowel. Form new words by putting each base word and suffix together. Write the new words on the lines.

1. scan + ing _____
2. fast + est _____
3. hot + est _____
4. sad + ness _____
5. steep + er _____
6. plot + ed _____
7. equip + ment _____
8. hard + ness _____

9. drip + ed _____
10. snap + ing _____
11. heart + less _____
12. wet + est _____
13. cram + ed _____
14. cheer + ful _____
15. rapid + ly _____
16. strap + ed _____

Circle the base word in each word in the word bank. Then complete each sentence with a word from the word bank.

throbbing	quitters	slipped	plugged
swimming	flippers	squatted	swimmer
raining	trapper	hottest	dimmest

17. We swam in the pool on the _____ day of the summer.

18. While I swam, I wore a face mask and _____.

19. Yesterday I _____ my ears, too.

20. I almost _____ when I walked onto the diving board.

21. We held a race to determine the fastest _____.

22. Our muscles were _____ from so much swimming.

23. If it isn't _____ tomorrow, we'll go back to the pool.

24. I sure hope we can go _____ again!

Lesson 62
Words that double the final consonant to add a suffix

Name _____

 Form new words by adding the correct suffixes.

> **RULE**
>
> When a word ends in **e**, drop the **e** before adding a suffix that begins with a vowel.
>
> like + **ing** = lik**ing**

	es	**ed**	**ing**
1. squeeze			
2. disapprove			
3. bribe			
4. hope			
5. imagine			

	er	**est**
6. late		
7. little		
8. humble		
9. nice		
10. strange		

Write the base word for each of the following words.

11. cradles	_____	**12.** safest	_____
13. approved	_____	**14.** decided	_____
15. observer	_____	**16.** combining	_____
17. pavement	_____	**18.** trader	_____
19. latest	_____	**20.** scrambled	_____
21. grazing	_____	**22.** candles	_____
23. sprinkler	_____	**24.** hiking	_____
25. changed	_____	**26.** liked	_____
27. scraping	_____	**28.** placing	_____

Underline the suffix **ing, ed, ion, able, ers** or **less** in each word below. Then write the base word on the line next to the word.

HINT

Remember that when a word ends in **e**, drop the **e** before adding a suffix that begins with a vowel.

1. strangers _____

2. debatable _____

3. making _____

4. increasing _____

5. believed _____

6. revision _____

7. imaginable _____

8. deciding _____

9. deceived _____

10. icing _____

11. fascination _____

12. shared _____

Use the base words you wrote to complete the crossword puzzle.

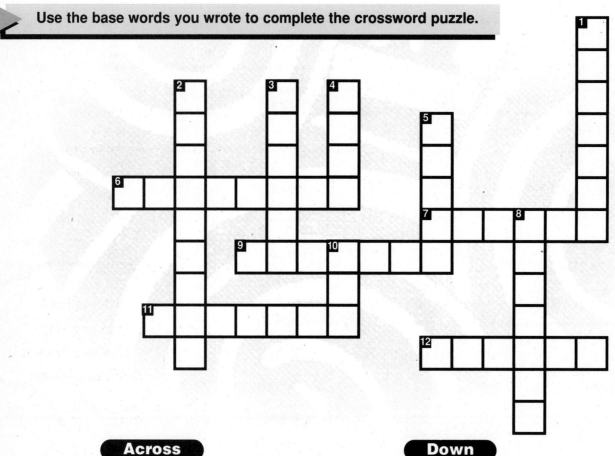

Across

6. to become greater or larger
7. to think about and change
9. to accept as true or real
11. not known before
12. to make up one's mind

Down

1. to lie or mislead
2. to interest very strongly
3. to argue for or against something
4. to put together; to create
5. to use something with another
8. to guess or suppose
10. solid water

Words that drop the final e to add a suffix

Name _____

Many words have more than one suffix. Read each word below. Underline the first suffix and circle the second suffix.

HINT

Remember that **s** can be a suffix.

watchfully   amazingly   painlessly

migrations   carelessness   widening

publications   frightfulness   enlightening

attractions   thoughtfulness   powerlessness

increasingly   cheerfulness   successfully

hopefully

Use a word from above to complete each sentence. Write the word on the line. Use each word only once.

1. Tracking migrating birds is becoming _____ popular.

2. The _____ of many birds take place in the spring and fall.

3. Some birds _____ fly over 5,000 miles yearly.

4. _____, some birds return to the same fields every year.

5. Studying migrating birds can be an _____ experience.

6. There are many _____ about birds.

7. Human _____ has blocked some migration paths.

8. The _____ of some groups has helped to protect birds.

9. Bird lovers watch the sky _____ every year.

Why do you think tracking migrating birds might be popular?

Critical Thinking

In each sentence, underline the two words with more than one suffix. Write each base word on a line next to the sentence.

1. When my mother awakened me today, I got out of bed cheerfully. _____ _____

2. Mom was heartened to see my fearlessness. _____ _____

3. I felt remarkably ready to thoughtfully begin my first volunteer job. _____ _____

4. Interestingly, my school project was to help the assistants at a senior center. _____ _____

5. My heartbeat quickened as I hesitatingly approached the center. _____ _____

6. I felt increasingly nervous as I opened the door carefully. _____ _____

7. My day passed painlessly and I enjoyed the loveableness of the people I met. _____ _____

8. Thankfully, my project is continuing successfully. _____ _____

9. The volunteer work I do is meaningful and enlightening—I love it! _____ _____

Circle each base word from the sentences above in the word search. The words may be horizontal, vertical or on the diagonal.

```
G  L  I  G  H  T  Q  U  I  C  K  I
U  Y  I  N  T  E  R  E  S  T  Q  N
A  W  A  K  E  Z  S  L  P  H  H  C
F  M  K  S  V  S  X  I  C  J  E  R
K  E  T  H  O  U  G  H  T  Q  A  E
R  I  A  X  B  C  J  M  L  A  R  A
E  N  G  R  W  C  V  H  E  O  T  S
M  C  P  F  G  E  A  Q  C  A  V  E
A  R  Q  A  I  S  J  R  H  K  N  E
R  A  S  S  I  S  T  S  E  R  S  Y
K  S  T  H  A  N  K  C  H  E  E  R
```

Name _____

Add s or es to write the plural form of each word.

chimney + S

1. story _____
2. canary _____
3. company _____
4. decoy _____
5. country _____
6. army _____
7. donkey _____
8. injury _____
9. victory _____
10. bay _____
11. holiday _____
12. missionary _____
13. valley _____
14. library _____
15. mystery _____
16. spy _____

Write the base word of each word below. Remember that each base word should end in y.

17. peppiest _____
18. dustier _____
19. mutinied _____
20. keyed _____
21. worrying _____
22. tardiest _____
23. rustier _____
24. flies _____
25. obeys _____
26. luckiest _____
27. fancier _____
28. multiplying _____
29. relayed _____
30. carried _____

Form a new word by combining each base word and suffix. Write the new word on the line.

Remember the rules for adding suffixes to words ending in **y**. **HINT**

1. lucky + er _____

2. greasy + est _____

3. worry + ed _____   **4.** busy + er _____

5. easy + er _____   **6.** salty + er _____

7. obey + s _____   **8.** toy + ed _____

9. occupy + ed _____   **10.** fancy + est _____

11. sleepy + est _____   **12.** heavy + er _____

Use the words you formed to complete the sentences. Then write the circled letters from the answers in order to answer the riddle.

13. Cinderella had the ◯ __ __ __ __ __ __ __ gown at the ball.

14. One little pig was ◯ __ __ __ __ __ __ than the other two.

15. Jack shouldn't have __ __ ◯ __ __ with the magic beans.

16. Hansel and Gretel visited a house __ __ __ __ ◯ __ __ __ by a witch.

17. Babe, the blue ox, made Paul Bunyan's work __ ◯ __ __ __ __ .

18. Rip Van Winkle is the __ __ __ __ ◯ __ __ __ character in any book.

19. The Brothers Grimm were __ __ __ __ ◯ __ than other authors.

20. The seven dwarfs __ __ ◯ __ __ __ about Snow White.

What is the best material for kites?

Riddle

Riddle answer: __ __ __ __ __ __ __ __ __

Name _____

> **Add ly to each word. Write the new word on the line.**

RULES

If a word ends in **y** and is preceded by a consonant, change the **y** to **i** when adding **ly**. If the **y** is preceded by a vowel, add **ly**. if a word ends in **le**, the **le** is dropped.

heavy + **ly** = heavi**ly**

coy + **ly** = coy**ly**

wobble + **ly** = wobb**ly**

1. noisy _____

2. coy _____

3. drizzle _____

4. greedy _____

5. bubble _____

6. dizzy _____

7. hasty _____

8. merry _____

9. probable _____

10. wiggle _____

11. pebble _____

12. lucky _____

> **Complete each sentence with a word from above.**

13. It was a _____ wet day, perfect for a trip to the indoor aquarium.

14. We could hear the sea lions barking _____ while we waited for tickets.

15. The aquarium was enormous, so we had to _____ view each exhibit.

16. The bottom of the largest aquarium tank was _____, and not covered with sand.

17. The diver's air tanks made the water _____.

18. The _____ arms of the squid grabbed everything in sight.

19. _____, the glass walls stopped it from grabbing us.

20. We watched the dolphins swim _____ round and round.

21. I'll _____ go back to the aquarium at least twice a year.

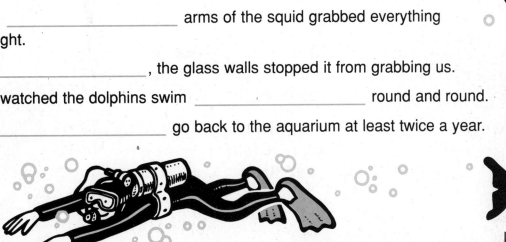

Adding suffix -ly to words ending in y or le

1. Eating _____ every day helps an athlete keep fit.
   (healthy)

2. A trainer should _____ supervise every workout.
   (reliable)

3. Proper training techniques can prevent _____ injury.
   (body)

4. Training _____ will not help an athlete.
   (lazy)

5. Jogging can strengthen _____ legs.
   (wobble)

6. If athletes practice _____, they will perform poorly.
   (sloppy)

7. Athletes should not begin weight training _____.
   (hasty)

8. They must always warm up _____.
   (sensible)

9. _____, many athletes are born with coordination.
   (Lucky)

10. People with good coordination can usually exercise more _____.
    (ready)

11. Athletes in good shape can do exercises _____.
    (easy)

12. Sometimes athletes should _____ take time off from training.
    (happy)

13. It is not necessary to exercise _____.
    (day)

14. Gymnasts can move _____ on the parallel bars.
    (nimble)

15. Athletes should accept both victory and defeat _____.
    (noble)

What do you think accepting both victory and defeat nobly means?

Critical Thinking

Name _____

Fill in the circle under the word that completes each sentence.

1. Ranchers spent much of their ____ moving cattle.

   ○ lives   ○ lifes   ○ lifves

2. Their ____ sometimes helped with the daily roundup.

   ○ wifes   ○ wives   ○ wiffes

3. The cowboys often carried buck ____ .

   ○ knives   ○ knifes   ○ kniffs

4. They wore scarves to protect ____ in dust storms.

   ○ themselfs   ○ themselves   ○ themselfes

5. The cowboys used dried ____ as fuel for campfires.

   ○ leafes   ○ leafs   ○ leaves

6. The cook brought ____ of bread.

   ○ loafs   ○ loaves   ○ loafes

7. Mountain ____ stopped the herds from stampeding.

   ○ cliffes   ○ cliffs   ○ clives

8. Sometimes the ____ were very steep.

   ○ bluffs   ○ bluffes   ○ bluves

9. The young ____ often fell behind the herd.

   ○ calfs   ○ calves   ○ calfes

10. The ranchers all shared similar ____ concerning cattle rustlers.

    ○ beliefs   ○ believes   ○ beliefes

11. Tribal leaders, or ____ , usually allowed the herds to pass.

    ○ chiefes   ○ chieves   ○ chiefs

12. Packs of ____ sometimes attacked the herds.

    ○ wolfes   ○ wolves   ○ wolfs

13. Cattle ____ , or rustlers, were also a problem.

    ○ thiefes   ○ thieves   ○ thiefs

What would you like about being a cowboy?

Critical Thinking

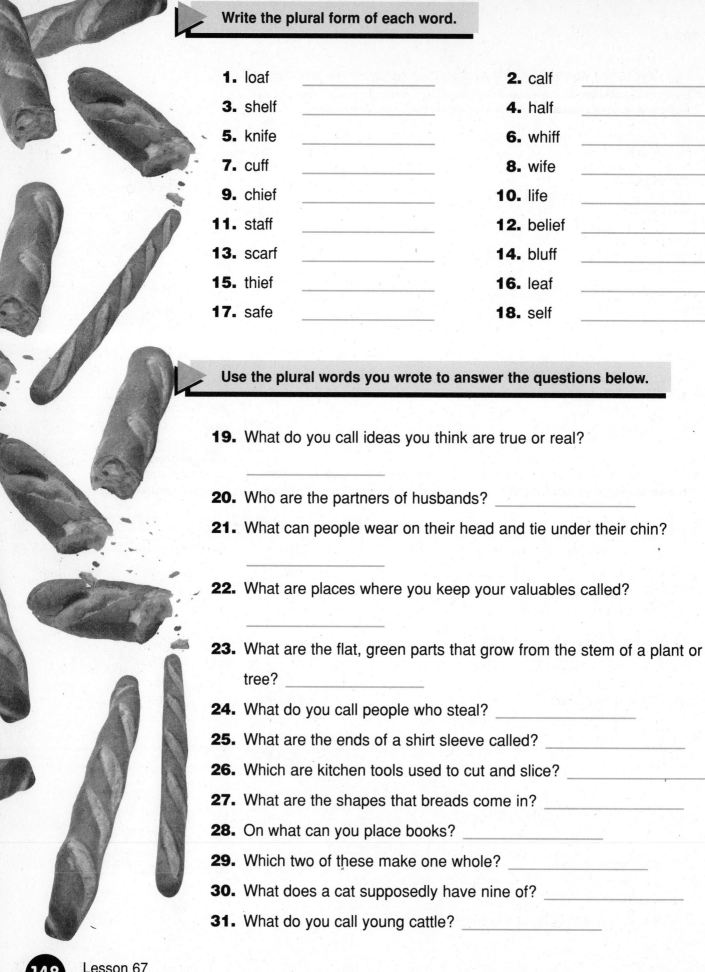

Write the plural form of each word.

1. loaf _____   2. calf _____
3. shelf _____   4. half _____
5. knife _____   6. whiff _____
7. cuff _____   8. wife _____
9. chief _____   10. life _____
11. staff _____   12. belief _____
13. scarf _____   14. bluff _____
15. thief _____   16. leaf _____
17. safe _____   18. self _____

Use the plural words you wrote to answer the questions below.

19. What do you call ideas you think are true or real?

_____

20. Who are the partners of husbands? _____

21. What can people wear on their head and tie under their chin?

_____

22. What are places where you keep your valuables called?

_____

23. What are the flat, green parts that grow from the stem of a plant or

tree? _____

24. What do you call people who steal? _____

25. What are the ends of a shirt sleeve called? _____

26. Which are kitchen tools used to cut and slice? _____

27. What are the shapes that breads come in? _____

28. On what can you place books? _____

29. Which two of these make one whole? _____

30. What does a cat supposedly have nine of? _____

31. What do you call young cattle? _____

Name _____

▷ **Write the plural of each word. You may use your dictionary if necessary.**

> **RULE**
>
> Many words that end in **o** form their plural by adding **s**. Some words form the plural by adding **es**.
>
> radio   radio**s**   potato   potato**es**
>
> tomato   tomato**es**

1. banjo _____
2. poncho _____
3. piccolo _____
4. patio _____
5. echo _____
6. hero _____
7. radio _____
8. rodeo _____
9. tempo _____
10. studio _____

11. solo _____
12. cello _____
13. piano _____
14. alto _____
15. photo _____

▷ **Choose the correct word to complete each sentence. Write the word on the line.**

16. Our music teacher told us to bring our _____ to class.
    (radios, rodeos)

17. We were studying elements of music, such as rhythms and _____.
    (patios, tempos)

18. The sound of twenty radios sent _____ through the classroom.
    (solos, echoes)

19. We learned that _____ are not used in symphony orchestras.
    (ponchos, banjos)

20. _____ look like violins, but are much bigger.
    (Cellos, Heroes)

21. There are eighty-eight keys on grand _____.
    (pianos, heroes)

22. We listened to _____ and guessed which instrument was playing.
    (solos, patios)

23. We could easily hear the shrill notes of the small _____.
    (photos, piccolos)

1. piano _____   2. alto _____
3. photo _____   4. igloo _____
5. piccolo _____   6. tornado _____
7. poncho _____   8. avocado _____
9. tomato _____   10. hero _____
11. banjo _____   12. cello _____
13. patio _____   14. rodeo _____
15. potato _____   16. kangaroo _____
17. studio _____   18. solo _____

Use the plural words you wrote to answer the questions below.

19. Which words name musical instruments? _____

_____   _____

20. What are outdoor courtyards? _____

21. What are competitions in which contestants ride horses and rope cattle called?

_____

22. What are terrible wind storms called? _____

23. What are people called who do brave and wonderful deeds?

_____

24. Which vegetable is used to make spaghetti sauce and ketchup?

_____

25. What are pictures taken with a camera called? _____

26. What are large, waterproof cloaks often worn by campers?

_____

27. What are dome-shaped huts made of snow? _____

28. Which vegetable can taste good in all these forms: mashed, french fried, baked,

and scalloped? _____

29. What are small rooms or buildings where artists work? _____

Name _____

These words are the same in their singular and plural forms. If the word names a plant or a food that comes from a plant, write **P**. If it names an animal or a food that comes from an animal, write **A**.

1. _____ spinach
2. _____ milk
3. _____ salmon
4. _____ zucchini
5. _____ moose
6. _____ sheep
7. _____ spaghetti
8. _____ shrimp
9. _____ cattle
10. _____ broccoli
11. _____ trout
12. _____ haddock
13. _____ deer
14. _____ popcorn
15. _____ honey
16. _____ bread
17. _____ rye
18. _____ bacon
19. _____ cod
20. _____ wheat
21. _____ butter
22. _____ sauerkraut
23. _____ fish
24. _____ oatmeal

Read each word, find its plural form in the word bank, and write the plural on the line beside the word. Then choose a word from the word bank to match each definition. Each singular form is given in parentheses.

fungi	geese	alumni	feet
women	oases	children	mice
teeth	men	oxen	crises

25. foot _____
26. man _____
27. child _____
28. woman _____
29. goose _____
30. mouse _____
31. ox _____
32. tooth _____

33. _____ times of danger or anxious waiting (crisis)
34. _____ people who have attended a school (alumnus)
35. _____ plants such as mushrooms and toadstools (fungus)
36. _____ places in the desert where there is water (oasis)

Word Bank

- sheep
- sauerkraut
- salmon
- cactuses
- women
- mice
- teeth
- oatmeal
- cattle
- wheat
- deer
- moose
- bacon
- men
- popcorn
- spaghetti
- milk
- crises
- geese

Across

4. farm animals sheared for their wool
5. salted, smoked meat often served with eggs
6. swift animals living in the woods
7. large ocean fish that swim up rivers to lay their eggs
8. cereal grasses used for making flour
9. cooked cereal made from ground, boiled oats
10. what you use to bite and chew food
11. more than one male
12. small rodents found in houses and fields
14. something to drink
15. stressful, anxious times

Down

1. animals of the cow family
2. large birds that honk and fly in V formations to migrate
3. corn that turns into white puffs when heated
4. cabbage that's spiced and tastes sour
7. noodles from Italy
8. more than one female
12. large woodland animals with wide antlers
13. prickly plants you wouldn't want to sit on

Name _____

 Study the rules. Then write the number of vowels you see, the number of vowel sounds you hear, and the number of syllables in each word. Remember that **y** is sometimes a vowel.

RULES

1. Double vowels stand for only one vowel sound.

   inst**ea**d   sp**oo**nful

2. A prefix or suffix is a syllable in itself if it has a vowel sound.

   prewash   old**en**

3. Some prefixes and suffixes have more than one vowel sound and therefore have more than one syllable.

   ultrafine   **super**human

	Vowels Seen	Vowel Sounds	Syllables		Vowels Seen	Vowel Sounds	Syllables
1. congratulations				19. insight			
2. encountered				20. exclamation			
3. exaggerating				21. kangaroos			
4. irresponsible				22. excitably			
5. determination				23. handkerchiefs			
6. indirectly				24. irritability			
7. invisible				25. resolution			
8. foreshadows				26. pavement			
9. imprisoned				27. organizations			
10. illogical				28. squeezing			
11. torpedoes				29. scrubber			
12. motionless				30. noisiest			
13. quickened				31. sleepily			
14. observer				32. entrusting			
15. combinations				33. feebly			
16. neighborhood				34. audible			
17. imagination				35. overcook			
18. peaceful				36. weighed			

Find the plural forms of twenty words in the puzzle. They appear horizontally or vertically, from left to right, or from top to bottom. Circle the words as you find them. Then list them below, dividing them into syllables using vertical lines.

```
P  C  F  C  A  C  T  U  S  E  S  Z
O  A  T  M  E  A  L  J  M  N  P  R
P  B  C  S  W  V  E  H  O  N  E  Y
C  U  E  P  A  I  R  S  A  U  P  E
O  T  D  A  B  C  H  E  R  O  E  S
R  T  F  G  P  I  C  C  O  L  O  S
N  E  H  H  M  I  Y  D  A  S  A  C
G  R  D  E  E  R  A  P  U  H  V  E
L  G  K  T  R  R  Y  O  C  E  E  L
C  O  D  T  O  M  A  T  O  E  S  L
C  Z  A  I  D  Z  O  A  L  P  E  O
M  A  P  B  C  A  T  T  L  E  O  S
S  H  R  I  M  P  E  O  B  T  K  N
G  U  O  Z  O  B  E  E  S  R  S  I
M  Z  R  O  D  E  O  S  B  M  N  O
```

_____   _____
_____   _____
_____   _____
_____   _____
_____   _____
_____   _____
_____   _____
_____   _____
_____   _____

Underline the compound words in the sentences. Then divide them into syllables by drawing vertical lines between the words that make up each compound.

> **RULE**
> Divide a compound word between the words that form the compound word.
> ear / drum   house / boat
> snow / flake

1. We must help safeguard the wildlife in national parks.

2. Protecting animals and plant life should be a lifelong effort.

3. Highways that run through park lands can destroy valuable land.

4. Landfills and airports near parks are dangerous to animals.

5. We should set aside park wetlands and backwoods just for wildlife.

6. Without laws and guidelines, some animals might become extinct.

7. Everyone needs to undertake the goal of protecting our environment.

Write these words on the lines below. Use vertical lines to divide them into syllables.

> **RULE**
> When a word ends in **le** preceded by a consonant, divide the word before that consonant.

baffle	purple	battle	dimple	puzzle	ample
mumble	fiddle	fumble	startle	grumble	crumble
cripple	jungle	cradle	angle	noble	gentle
people	wobble	bottle	paddle	handle	poodle

On the first line after each word, write the number of syllables. On the second line, divide the word into syllables using vertical lines.

HINT

A word has as many syllables as it has vowel sounds. Some prefixes and suffixes can have more than one syllable.

1. skyscraper _____ _____

2. wondering _____ _____

3. famous _____ _____

4. watermelon _____ _____

5. insects _____ _____

6. sofa _____ _____

7. strawberries _____ _____

8. startle _____ _____

9. wiggle _____ _____

10. butterfly _____ _____

11. tablespoon _____ _____

12. prisons _____ _____

13. wintertime _____ _____

14. windowpane _____ _____

15. shopkeeper _____ _____

16. shipmate _____ _____

17. stepladder _____ _____

18. hunger _____ _____

19. taxation _____ _____

20. recess _____ _____

21. sudden _____ _____

22. whistle _____ _____

23. poodle _____ _____

24. giggled _____ _____

25. protest _____ _____

Lesson 71
Syllabicating compound words and words with prefixes and suffixes

Name _____

WILMA MANKILLER

The Cherokee is one of the largest Native American nations in the United States. In recent years the Cherokee Nation of Oklahoma has grown stronger thanks to the leadership of their former principal chief, Wilma Mankiller. When elected to this position in 1985, Ms. Mankiller became the first woman to hold this title for the Cherokee Nation of Oklahoma.

Wilma Pearl Mankiller was born in Stillwell, Oklahoma, in 1945, one of 11 children. As a young wife and mother, she became interested in Native American problems. After graduating from college in 1977, she worked hard for the people of the Cherokee Nation. As a community development director, she successfully planned and built water systems in the dry lands and improved housing and roads.

When she was first elected principal chief, many Cherokee doubted that Ms. Mankiller was the right choice to lead them. However, her hard work and dedication to making life better proved the doubters wrong. In fact, she served two more terms as principal chief. Although a medical problem prevented her from serving a fourth term, Ms. Mankiller remains an active spokesperson for Native American issues.

What impresses you most about Wilma Mankiller?

_____
_____
_____
_____
_____
_____
_____

 **Writing**

 Write a speech encouraging students in your school to be more active in school government. Use words from the word bank and helpful hints to help you.

Why be more active?
What can you do?
How can you start?

 **Helpful Hints**

beliefs	increasingly	rapidly
biggest	lives	thoughtfulness
heroes	people	sensibly
imaginable	helpful	crises

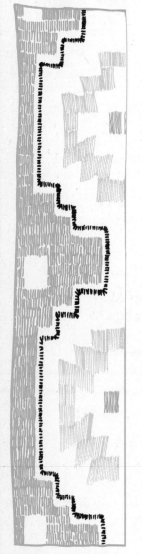

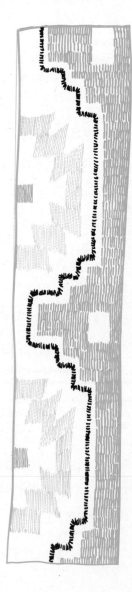

Lesson 72
Review suffixes and irregular plurals: Writing

Name

Fill in the circle beside the word that is correctly divided into syllables.

1. ○ won/der/ing   ○ wonder/ing   ○ wond/ering
2. ○ oa/tmeal   ○ oatm/eal   ○ oat/meal
3. ○ cact/us/es   ○ cac/tus/es   ○ cact/u/ses
4. ○ peop/le   ○ peo/ple   ○ pe/ople
5. ○ butt/er/fly   ○ butter/fly   ○ but/ter/fly
6. ○ pic/co/los   ○ picc/olos   ○ picco/los

Fill in the circle beside the plural form for each word in dark print.

7. **potato**   ○ potato   ○ potatos   ○ potatoes
8. **piano**   ○ pianos   ○ pianoes   ○ pianist
9. **life**   ○ lives   ○ lifes   ○ lifves
10. **hero**   ○ hero   ○ heroes   ○ heroe
11. **child**   ○ childes   ○ children   ○ childrens
12. **half**   ○ halves   ○ halfs   ○ halfes
13. **sheep**   ○ sheepes   ○ sheep   ○ sheeps
14. **leaf**   ○ leafs   ○ leafes   ○ leaves

Read each sentence and the two groups of suffixes that follow it. Notice the base word in dark print. Fill in the circle beside the suffix in each group that belongs in each blank. Then read the sentence again to make sure it makes sense.

15. Thomas Edison's **invent** _____ _____
    a   b
    is admired by all.
    a. ○ ful ○ ly ○ ive ○ ness
    b. ○ ful ○ ly ○ ive ○ ness

16. He chose to work on **seem** _____ _____
    a   b
    impossible tasks.
    a. ○ ing ○ able ○ ly ○ ible
    b. ○ ing ○ able ○ ly ○ ible

17. Edison **success** _____ _____ patented
    a   b
    1,033 inventions in all!
    a. ○ ion ○ ful ○ ness ○ ly
    b. ○ ion ○ ful ○ ness ○ ly

Read the words in the word bank. Then read the story. Write the correct word from the word bank on the line to complete each unfinished sentence. Then answer the questions.

beliefs	bounties	concentrated	debated	dedicated	defenseless
development	endangered	experiencing	observers	ranchers	wolves

Wolves Ahead

In the 1800s, thousands of _____ roamed North America. Today, biologists consider gray and red wolves _____ in 48 states. Only about 9,000 wolves still live in the wild, _____ mostly in Alaska and Minnesota. However, biologists have been _____ success in reintroducing the gray wolf and the red wolf into their former ranges.

For a long time people believed that wolves were dangerous because they attacked _____ sheep and cattle. So local, state, and federal governments offered _____ for wolves. These animals were killed by hunting, trapping, and poisoning. However, research from scientific _____ has found that these _____ about wolves are generally untrue.

In 1995, _____ scientists released several gray wolves into Yellowstone National Park as an experiment. These were the first wolves in the park since 1926 Farmers and _____ who live near the park are wary of this _____, so the experiment will continue to be _____

1. How do scientists know that the reintroduction of wolves in certain areas has been successful?

_____

_____

2. Are people interested in saving the wolf? How can you tell?

_____

_____

Alphabetizing, Multi-meaning Words

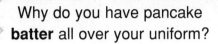

Why do you have pancake **batter** all over your uniform?

What do you mean, I am the **batter!**

She hit the ball so hard the **hide** split!

She didn't **hide!** She's on second base!

What is the **key** to winning the game?

I know! Finding the **key** to the equipment closet!

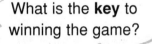

COACH

The same word can have more than one meaning. How did this lead to misunderstandings?

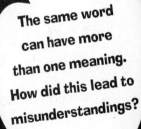

Let's play the **rest** of the game!

Don't **rest** yet! We have to win first!

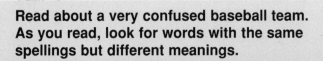
Read about a very confused baseball team. As you read, look for words with the same spellings but different meanings.

Critical Thinking

Home Letter

Dear Family,

In the next few weeks, your child will be learning dictionary skills such as alphabetizing words, using guide words to find dictionary entries more easily, and distinguishing between words that may have more than one meaning, such as tire and band.

At-Home Activities

▶ With your child, read the comic strip on the other side of this letter. Talk about the different meanings of the boldfaced words.

▶ Suggest that your child practice alphabetizing skills by looking up friends' names in the telephone book. Together, make a personal or family telephone directory.

▶ Make up jokes or puns with some of the multiple-meaning words—or create new cartoon pictures that could illustrate them.

Book Corner

You and your child might enjoy reading these books together. Look for them in your local library.

Every Living Thing

by Cynthia Rylant

Relationships and interactions between people and animals are skillfully depicted in this short story collection.

Home-Run Hitters

by John A. Torres

The author chronicles the history of baseball while exploring the careers of the players who have hit four home runs in one game.

Sincerely,

_____

Name _____

RULE

When words begin with the same letter or letters, look at the second or third letter to put the words in alphabetical order.

1

microphone _____

middle _____

mistake _____

mystery _____

morning _____

modern _____

2

swaying _____

strawberry _____

seashore _____

skateboard _____

sickness _____

3

awkward _____

arrive _____

amount _____

application _____

aching _____

4

crayon _____

creek _____

crusty _____

cringe _____

crock _____

5

lotion _____

loneliness _____

locust _____

loaves _____

loyalty _____

6

southerly _____

sorrow _____

socialize _____

sometime _____

softening _____

7

blond _____

battery _____

blanket _____

bulge _____

beach _____

bath _____

8

thaw _____

trio _____

tunnel _____

tumble _____

talent _____

thief _____

9

payment _____

position _____

planter _____

pension _____

prance _____

Draw a line from each pair of guide words on the left to the word on the right that would be found on that dictionary page. The first one shows you what to do.

1. belt/bind   rink
   mine/moon   stand
   olive/ox   moan
   quack/quietly   bend
   stamp/star   quick
   raid/robe   open

2. back/bag   basket
   baseball/battle   blink
   beat/behind   badge
   blanket/block   better
   bonnet/bought   begin
   belief/beware   bother

Read the guide words at the top of each column. Circle the one word in the column that would <u>not</u> be on the same dictionary page as those guide words.

3 **a/aid**	4 **each/east**	5 **ladder/let**
afraid	easel	last
about	eagle	list
ache	eat	lead
also	ear	lamp
address	ease	leap

6 **dear/dish**	7 **imagine/increase**	8 **stage/storage**
deliver	indeed	still
deep	immediately	steep
ditch	imitate	stung
destroy	include	stick
dimple	incident	stand

Name _____

Study the pronunciation key. Then follow the directions below.

The respelling that follows a dictionary entry shows how to pronounce the word. Use the pronunciation key in the dictionary to help you pronounce each respelling.

Vowels

Symbol	Key Words	Symbol	Key Words
a	cat	oo	look, pull
ā	ape	ōo	tool, rule
ä	cot, car	ou	out, crowd
e	ten, berry	u	up
ē	me	ʉr	fur, shirt
i	fit, here	ə	a in ago
ī	ice, fire		e in agent
ō	go		i in pencil
ô	fall, for		o in atom
oi	oil		u in circus

Consonants

Symbol	Key Words	Symbol	Key Words
b	bed	s	see
d	dog	t	top
f	fall	v	vat
g	get	w	wish
h	help	y	yard
j	jump	z	zebra
k	kill, call	ch	chin, arch
l	leg	ŋ	ring, drink
m	meat	sh	she, push
n	nose	th	thin, truth
p	put	*th*	then, father
r	red	zh	measure

Read the respellings below. Notice the symbols in color. Beside each respelling write the words from the pronunciation key that show how to pronounce that symbol. Then write the entry word for each respelling.

1. lēf _____ _____

2. round _____ _____

3. *th*ōz _____ _____

4. bʉrn _____ _____

5. koil _____ _____

6. pōol _____ _____

7. sôrs _____ _____

8. nōoz _____ _____

9. äks _____ _____

10. fʉrst _____ _____

Use the pronunciation key on page 165 and accent marks to pronounce each respelling below. Circle the syllable that is said with more stress, and then rewrite the word showing the correct spelling. You may use your dictionary if necessary.

HINT

When a word has two or more syllables, one syllable is stressed, or accented, more than any other. In the dictionary, an accent mark (´) shows the syllable that is said with more stress.

1. rēd´ iŋ _____

2. trub´ əl _____

3. man´ ij ər _____

4. mem´ ərē _____

5. rē välv´ _____

6. *th*er with´ _____

7. di stʉrb´ _____

8. bil´ dər _____

9. un luk´ ē _____

10. rē fresh´ mənt _____

11. flɷn´ dər _____

12. kə rir´ _____

13. ə thôr´ ə tē _____

14. kan´ dəl _____

15. gär´ bij _____

Use the pronunciation key on page 165 and accent marks to pronounce each respelling below. Then circle the word at the right that goes with that respelling.

16. sim´ pəl	simmer	single	simple
17. də zurv´	deserve	desert	dessert
18. pas´ chər	pasture	patch	pastel
19. ə slēp´	assure	ashamed	asleep
20. baj	bug	badge	bus
21. thʉr´ o	theron	thought	thorough
22. jin´ jər	jungle	ginger	garage
23. ek splō´ zhən	explain	sxploring	explosion
24. sɷt´ ə bəl	suited	suite	suitable
25. ga*th*´ ə riŋ	gathering	gardenia	getaway

Name

For each group of words, match the word in boldface print with its respelling. Write the letter of the correct respelling beside the word. Use the pronunciation key below and accent marks as a guide.

a	cat	o	go		ʉr	fur, shirt	ə =	**a** in **a**go
a	ape	ô	fall, for		ch	**ch**in, ar**ch**		**e** in agent
ä	cot, car	oi	oil		ŋ	ri**ng**, dri**nk**		**i** in pencil
e	ten, berry	͝oo	look, pull		sh	**sh**e, pu**sh**		**o** in atom
ē	me	͞oo	tool, rule		th	**th**in, tru**th**		**u** in circ**u**s
i	fit, here	ou	out, crowd		_th_	**th**en, fa**th**er		
ī	ice, fire	u	up		zh	mea**s**ure		

_____ **1.** anchor   a. prē zʉrv´

_____ **2.** preserve   b. j͞oo´ əl

_____ **3.** hayfield   c. drôr

_____ **4.** drawer   d. hā´ fēld

_____ **5.** jewel   e. aŋ´ kər

_____ **6.** second   a. lik´ wid

_____ **7.** liquid   b. ē nôr´ məs

_____ **8.** enormous   c. gʉr´ gəl

_____ **9.** loosen   d. l͞oos´ ən

_____ **10.** gurgle   e. sek´ ənd

Use the pronunciation key and the accent marks to say the respellings. Fill in the circle next to the word that is the correct match for each respelling.

11. kär t͞oon´
- ○ carton
- ○ cartoon

12. grāz
- ○ graze
- ○ grass

13. kwit
- ○ quite
- ○ quit

14. pouns
- ○ pounds
- ○ pounce

15. hwin
- ○ whine
- ○ win

16. jäk´ ē
- ○ joke
- ○ jockey

17. n͞ooz
- ○ nose
- ○ news

18. sə ment´
- ○ comment
- ○ cement

19. hōz
- ○ hose
- ○ house

20. nīs
- ○ nice
- ○ niece

Twelve words are hidden in the puzzle. The words may be written across, down, or diagonally. Circle each word and write it on the first line next to its definition. On the second line, write the word as a dictionary entry word.

HINT

Entry words are often listed in the dictionary without suffixes such as **s, es, ed,** or **ing.** When you search for a word in the dictionary, look for the word without these suffixes.

```
V I S I T O R S Z C
W A L K E D W L V R
K D X H E R O E S O
N A K T S F C E G W
I N Z L G H L P Q N
V C T R O P H I E S
E I J T Z A K N E P
S N X J M N V G J S
V G C O A C H E S R
E R A S I N G P S Q
```

1. awards _____ _____

2. moving your body to music _____ _____

3. guests _____ _____

4. worn by kings and queens _____ _____

5. being in a state of rest _____ _____

6. breads before they are sliced _____ _____

7. traveled on foot _____ _____

8. trainers for sports activities _____ _____

9. moves through the air _____ _____

10. exceptional and brave people _____ _____

11. the act of removing something _____ _____

12. utensils used to cut food _____ _____

Name _____

Read the dictionary entries. Decide which meaning of a word is used in each sentence below. Write the correct word and its definition number.

When there is more than one meaning for an entry word, the different meanings are numbered. The most commonly used meaning is usually listed first.

band (bānd) *n.* 1 a cord or wire, or a strip of some material, used to encircle something or to bind something together 2 a stripe of some different color or material 3 a group of persons united for a purpose 4 a group of musicians playing together *v.* 5 to unite in a band

fly (flī) *v.* 1 to move through the air by using wings 2 to travel through air in an aircraft or spacecraft 3 to cause to fly in the air 4 to move swiftly 5 to wave or flutter in the air, as a flag

interest (in´ trist *or* in´ tə rəst) *n.* 1 a feeling of wanting to know, learn, see, or take part in something 2 a share in something 3 money paid for the use of someone else's money *v.* 4 to cause to care about or join in

serve (surv) *v.* 1 to work or work for as a servant 2 to promote the interest of; work for; aid; help 3 to perform a duty or function

train (trān) *n.* 1 a line of railway cars coupled together and operated as a unit 2 a line of vehicles, pack animals, or persons traveling together *v.* 3 to instruct or drill for a special purpose

1. During World War II (1941–1945), African American pilots wanted to _____ their country.

2. They thought their _____ in flying would be useful to the army.

3. The pilots wanted to _____ planes in combat for the U.S. Army Air Corps.

4. At that time, African Americans could not _____ as pilots.

5. African American leaders decided to _____ together.

6. Their aim was to _____ the president in desegregating the armed forces.

7. In 1941 the army established a flight school at Tuskegee Institute, in Alabama, to _____ African American pilots.

8. This small _____ of pilots went on to make history.

9. While _____ played, the Tuskegee airmen received medals for their heroism and bravery during the war.

10. They were proud to see the American flag _____ in parades in their honor at the end of the war.

HINT

Sometimes a word has a small raised number to the right of it. This indicates that there is another word pronounced and spelled the same way, but with a completely different meaning or origin.

hatch[1] (hach) *v.* to bring forth young birds, fish, turtles, etc. from eggs [Birds hatch their eggs by keeping them warm]

hatch[2] (hach) *n.* an opening in the deck of a ship, such as one through which cargo is moved into and out of the hold.

post[1] (pōst) *n.* a long, thick piece of wood, metal, or other material set upright for holding something up, such as a building, sign, fence, and so on

post[2] (pōst) *n.* the place where a soldier, guard, etc. is on duty [The sentry walks a *post* just over the hill.]

rank[1] (raŋk) *n.* a row of soldiers, vehicles, and so on, placed side by side

rank[2] (raŋk) *adj.* having a strong, unpleasant taste or smell [*rank* fish]

stall[1] (stôl) *n.* a section for one animal in a stable

stall[2] (stôl) *v.* to hold off by sly or clever means; delay by evading [He *stalled* for time.]

tire[1] (tir) *v.* to make or become unable to go on because of a need for rest; exhaust [The hike *tired* me.]

tire[2] (tir) *n.* a solid rubber hoop or tube filled with air, fixed around the rim of a wheel

1. Terry wrinkled his nose because the air smelled

   _____.

2. He hadn't cleaned Sparky's _____ in two days.

3. Terry realized that he couldn't _____ any

   longer.

4. Terry hitched Sparky to a _____ while he

   did his chores.

5. Before he left the barn, he watched some chicks

   _____.

6. Later, on the way to school, he waved to a crossing guard

   at her _____.

7. Ten blocks from school, Terry's bicycle

   _____ went flat.

8. The whole experience was enough

   to _____ Terry by the time he got to school.

Name _____

Reading ▶ **Read the following article. Then answer the question.**

What's Real?

Whatever your opinion about electronic games, they are here to stay. Video games, also called electronic games, appeared in arcades in the early 1970s. The first commercially successful video game was Atari's *Pong*, released in 1972. As millions of young people flocked to the arcades, programmers created new games to keep their fans interested.

In the late 1970s and early 1980s, advances in computer technology allowed game programmers to improve and add better video, graphics, sound, and speed. Games such as *Donkey Kong* and *Super Mario Brothers* benefited from these advances.

In the 1990s the further miniaturization and improvement of components changed video games even more. Early video games relied on 8-bit processors; today, 32-bit based video game systems are common, with 64-bit game systems ready to be introduced. A 64-bit video game processes information 700 percent faster than an 8-bit video game! This processing speed allows stunning images, 3-D graphics, and realistic sound effects.

No matter how realistic it seems, electronic games can't take the place of the real world. An electronic game can bewilder, challenge, dazzle, educate, and grab your attention—but it's still just a game.

START **1,000 PTS.**

GAME OVER

What do you think the next generation of video games will be like?

_____
_____
_____
_____
_____
_____

Writing

It's 2015 and you've just been selected to interview the current video game wizard. Write an article describing what you learned about the wizard's new games. Use the helpful hints below and five words from the word bank.

command

computer

create

electronic

game

imagine

industry

learn

picture   realistic

technology   think

Helpful Hints

- **What is the subject of the games?**
- **What type of graphics and sound effects are used?**
- **Who is the audience?**
- **What will users of the games learn?**

Fill in the circle beside the group of words that is in alphabetical order.

1. ○ back, bump, break
    ○ rely, relay, relief
    ○ mesh, mess, messy

2. ○ cater, cease, circle
    ○ clasp, clash, crash
    ○ chick, check, clock

3. ○ merely, merry, merit
    ○ merry, merit, merely
    ○ merely, merit, merry

4. ○ short, sport, snort
    ○ spin, span, spun
    ○ invert, invest, invoke

5. ○ heart, heal, hearth
    ○ heal, heart, hearth
    ○ hearth, heart, heal

6. ○ coral, cord , cook
    ○ cook, coral, cord
    ○ cook, cord , coral

7. ○ pass, passage, passageway
    ○ passage, passageway, pass
    ○ passageway, pass, passage

8. ○ silo, silt, silly
    ○ silly, silo, silt
    ○ silt, silly, silo

9. ○ stick, sticker, sticky
    ○ sticker, sticky, stick
    ○ stick, sticky, sticker

10. ○ egg, eel, eight
    ○ eight, egg, eel
    ○ eel, egg, eight

Fill in the circle under the word that would be found on the same page as the guide words in dark print.

11. **hew/high**
    ○ hers   ○ hide   ○ hero

12. **refill/refrain**
    ○ refer   ○ reflex   ○ reed

13. **imprint/in**
    ○ improper ○ impress   ○ inactive

14. **tactics/take**
    ○ tag   ○ tact   ○ tale

15. **mail/make**
    ○ major   ○ maple   ○ magnet

16. **family/fast**
    ○ fame   ○ fawn   ○ fancy

17. **pupil/pursue**
    ○ purpose   ○ punch   ○ pup

18. **bright/bring**
    ○ brick   ○ brim   ○ brisk

19. **contest/contract**
    ○ context   ○ control   ○ contrite

20. **fold/foot**
    ○ for   ○ folk   ○ football

Lesson 79
Alphabetizing, multi-meaning words: Checkup

173

 Read the words in the word bank. Then read the story. Write the correct word from the word bank on the line to complete each unfinished sentence. Then answer the questions.

born	fifty	career	instrument
culture	interpretations	directed	popular
discovered	symphony	excelled	woman

The First Lady of Song

Ella Fitzgerald is the African American _____ known as the First Lady of Song. The popular jazz singer was _____ in Virginia in 1918. She was first _____ when she was 16 and won a talent show in Harlem, a center for African American life and _____ in New York City. She began her actual singing _____ in 1935 as the singer in a jazz band. When the band leader died, she _____ the band.

This jazz great toured the world for over _____ years. She performed with big bands, _____ orchestras, and in solo appearances. She is best known for the clear tones of her voice and her personal _____ of jazz and popular songs. She _____ at scat singing, using the voice as an _____ by singing improvised syllables instead of words.

Although she died in 1996, Ella Fitzgerald's music is still _____ with people who love to listen to jazz. Her unique style continues to entertain her fans.

1. Why do you think Ella Fitzgerald is known as the First Lady of Song?

_____

_____

2. Why was Ella Fitzgerald a popular singer? Explain your answer.

_____

_____

Definitions

◆ **Analogy:** Tells the relationship that one thing has to another. (kitten is to cat as puppy is to dog)

◆ **Antonyms:** Words that have opposite or almost opposite meanings.

◆ **Apostrophe:** This mark (') is an apostrophe. An apostrophe can be added to a word to show possession—that someone or something owns or has something. (Ellen's book) An apostrophe can also be used to stand for the missing letters in a contraction. (isn't = is not)

◆ **Base Word:** A word to which a prefix or suffix may be added to form a new word. (**print**er, un**pack**, **like**ly)

◆ **Compound Word:** A word that is made up of two smaller words. Each small word can stand alone and still have meaning. (dog + house = **doghouse**)

◆ **Consonant(s):** The letters of the alphabet except **a, e, i, o,** and **u.** The letter **y** can be either a consonant or a vowel, depending on its sound in a word.

◆ **Consonant Blend:** In a consonant blend, two or more consonants are sounded together so that each consonant can be heard. (**bl**ack, **tr**ain, **spr**ing, fa**st**, la**mp**)

◆ **Consonant Digraph:** In a consonant digraph, two consonants are sounded together to make one sound. (**wh**en, **th**in, **ch**in, **sh**eep, clo**th**, pa**ck**)

◆ **Contraction:** A short way to write two words. The two words are written together, leaving out one or more letters. An apostrophe stands for the missing letters.

◆ **Diphthong:** In a diphthong, two letters are blended together to make one vowel sound. (cl**ou**d, b**oy**, **oi**l, c**ow**, n**ew**)

◆ **Homographs:** Words that are spelled the same, but have different meanings and different word backgrounds. Some homographs have different pronunciations.

◆ **Homonyms:** Words that sound alike but have different meanings. They may or may not have different spellings.

◆ **Main Idea:** A main idea sentence tells what a paragraph is about.

◆ **Prefix:** A word part that is added at the beginning of a base or root word to change the word's meaning or form a new word. (**re**cycle, **un**wrap, **dis**appear)

◆ **Root:** A word part to which a prefix or suffix may be added to form a new word. (intro**duct**ion, pro**spect**or, re**duce**)

◆ **Suffix:** A word part that is added at the end of a root or base word to change the word's meaning or the way it is used. (sprint**er**, dark**ness**, help**ful**)

◆ **Syllable:** A word or word part with a single vowel sound.

◆ **Synonym(s):** Words that have the same or almost the same meaning.

◆ **Vowel(s):** The letters **a, e, i, o,** and **u.** The letter **y** can also be a vowel when **y** has the long **i** or long **e** sound.

◆ **Vowel Digraph:** In a vowel digraph, two vowels together can make a long or short sound or have a special sound all of their own. Vowel digraphs don't follow the long vowel rules. [br**ea**k (ā), h**ea**d (e)]

◆ **Vowel Pair:** In a vowel pair, two vowels come together to make one long vowel sound. The first vowel stands for the long sound, and the second vowel is silent. [**ai**m (ā), pl**ay** (ā)]

General Rules

► **Short-Vowel Rule:** If a word or syllable has only one vowel and it comes at the beginning or between two consonants, the vowel is usually short. (**a**m, **i**s, b**a**g, f**o**x)

► **Long-Vowel Rule 1:** If a syllable has two vowels, the first vowel is usually long and the second vowel is silent. (r**ai**n, k**i**t**e**, c**a**n**e**, j**ee**p, r**ay**)

► **Long-Vowel Rule 2:** If a word or syllable has one vowel and it comes at the end of the word or syllable, the vowel is usually long. (w**e**, g**o** p**o**ny)

► **Y as a Vowel Rules:**

1) If **y** is the only vowel at the end of a one-syllable word, **y** has the sound of **long i**. (fl**y**, b**y**)

2) If **y** is the only vowel at the end of a word of more than one syllable, **y** usually has the sound of **long e.** (sill**y**, bab**y**)

► **Soft C and G Rule:** When **c** or **g** is followed by **e**, **i**, or **y**, it is usually soft. (i**c**e, **c**ity, chan**g**e, **g**ym)

► **To Make a Word Plural:**

1) Usually just add **s**. (cat**s**, dog**s**, kite**s**)

2) If a word ends in **x**, **z**, **ss**, **sh**, or **ch**, usually add **es**. (fox**es**, dress**es**, peach**es**)

3) If a word ends in **y** preceded by a consonant, change the **y** to **i** and add **es**. (fl**ies**, fair**ies**, bab**ies**)

4) If a word ends in **f** or **fe**, usually change the **f** or **fe** to **v** and add **es**. (wolf/wol**ves**, knife/kni**ves**)

5) If a word ends in **o**, usually just add **s** to make the word plural. Some words are made plural by adding **es**. (potato/potato**es**, tomato/tomato**es**, hero/hero**es**)

6) Some words change their vowel sound in the plural form. (man/**men**, tooth/**teeth**, mouse/**mice**)

► **To Add Other Suffixes**

1) When a short-vowel word ends in a single consonant, usually double the consonant before adding a suffix that begins with a vowel. (ru**nning**, hu**mmed**, ba**tter**)

2) When a word ends in silent **e**, drop the **e** before adding a suffix that begins with a vowel. (bak**ing**, tap**ed**, lat**est**)

3) When a word ends in **y** preceded by a consonant, change the **y** to **i** before adding a suffix other than **ing**. (cr**ied**, happ**ily**, funn**ier**, pon**ies**) For the suffix **ing** do not change the **y** to **i**. (cry**ing**, try**ing**)

► **To Make a Noun Show Possession:**

1) Add **'s** to a singular noun. (dog**'s**, James**'s**, child**'s**)

2) Add an apostrophe only to a plural noun that ends in **s**. (boy**s'**, the Brown**s'**, babie**s'**)

3) Add **'s** to a plural noun that does not end in **s**. (mice**'s**, children**'s**, women**'s**)